NUMBER 12

New American Review

A Touchstone Book
Published by
Simon and Schuster

Distributed in UK and British Commonwealth
by Secker & Warburg

NEW AMERICAN REVIEW
Editor: Theodore Solotaroff
Poetry Editor: Richard Howard
Associate Editor: Daniel Moses
Assistant to the Editor: Rhoma Paul

Editorial Committee: Jonathan Dolger, Daniel Green, Julie Houston, Janet Kole, Michael V. Korda, Jeanette Mall, Alix Nelson, Diane Neustadter, Eugene Rachlis, William H. Simon

Production Associates: Frank Metz (art), Helen Barrow (design), Suzanne Frisbie, Susan Edwards, Tom Kieran, Ruth Randall

Cover design by Fred Otnes

A Touchstone Book
Published by Simon and Schuster
Rockefeller Center, 630 Fifth Avenue
New York, New York 10020

Distributed throughout the United Kingdom, the British Commonwealth (excluding Canada) and Europe by Martin Secker & Warburg Limited.

FIRST PRINTING

SBN 671–21032–7 Touchstone paperback edition
Library of Congress Catalog Card Number: 67–27377
Manufactured in the United States of America

The editors invite submissions. Manuscripts will
not be returned unless accompanied
by stamped self-addressed envelope.

Contents

Contents 3

Editors' Notes

EVERY SO OFTEN, *an author, a subject, and an occasion come together with a perfect kind of rightness, as though, for just this time, the normal uncertainties and approximations of writing have been swept aside. Everything is on target; nothing is wasted. Such prose, or poetry, seems to have behind it great reserves of primed consciousness: the force and economy of language being a function of all that the writer could say, knowing what he knows, feeling what he feels, and having waited until the time when he was ready. A. Alvarez's memoir of Sylvia Plath, which opens this issue, is a notable example.*

Though his essay runs to only 12,000 words, it has the weight of a much longer study. Like Gorky's memoir of Tolstoy, it not only describes a writer but manages to convey his presence in the world. Most biographical writing falls far short of this effect. The material, mostly researched data and documents, is fed into a process by which a life is furnished again with its events and works, through which the biographer conducts us like a family retainer, which he often is. Or there is the standard memoir: relatively flat and composed impressions, as though the writer were snapping pictures of his memories. In the case of someone like Sylvia Plath, there is also another kind of biographical writing which makes the figure into a statue and her life its shrine. All three approaches lack imagination.

During the last three years of Sylvia Plath's life, Alvarez was a friend of hers and of her husband, Ted Hughes. As a highly partisan critic, Alvarez was involved with their poetry, seeing early in Hughes's work and later in Sylvia Plath's a fierce vitality that supported him in the campaign he was waging against the academicism of contemporary poetry. He was also involved with their lives, in the way in which one can be with certain friends whose lives are so distinctively and deeply lived that they loom as emblems of contemporary experience and morale. And, as a "member of the club," as he puts it, Alvarez was caught up by Sylvia Plath's preoccupation with suicide.

From the content and course of these involvements, fleshed out by an imaginative vision of the relevant details, Alvarez has, quite simply, brought Sylvia Plath back to her life in these thirty pages, the last ten of which are devoted to the final months, and match in their own intensity the great, harrowing poems that she wrote during this time. In the course of describing the intentions and the circumstances of her death, Alvarez puts them in a radically different perspective from that of the received view of her suicide. And, in general, he strips away the misleading pathos of myth and cult that has obscured the figure of Sylvia Plath, and he enables her life and her poetry to come into the true and tragic light that she cast.

NAR 12 is graced by a second long essay, "A Course in Film-Making," by Norman Mailer. Here, too, writer and subject meet in a singularly apt way, for it is hard to believe that a film has ever been made, or is likely to be, by a director who is as articulate and inquisitive in telling the tale of its making as Mailer is. In order to focus the experience of filming Maidstone, his third and by far most complex film, Mailer develops the ground of his intention, to make a "pure" film, one that makes the fullest possible use of the evocativeness, fluidity, and uncertainty of the medium and that refuses to foreclose any of these possibilities by adulterating his film with the foreign agents of theater—a prepared plot, characterizations, dialogue, rehearsed performances, etc. So Mailer's "argument" for Maidstone leads him into an investigation of the radical differences between film and theater (and its Hollywood surrogate "filmed theater"), and then on to a definition of film that places it with its psychic counterparts, memory

(Continued on page 243)

NUMBER 12

New American Review

Sylvia Plath: A Memoir

A. Alvarez

As I REMEMBER it, I met Sylvia and her husband in London in the spring of 1960. My first wife and I were living near Swiss Cottage, on the unsmart edge of literary Hampstead, in a tall Edwardian building of particularly ugly red brick; it was the color of some old boiler that had been left out to rust for so long that even the brightness of decay had worn off. When we moved in, the place had just been converted by one of those grab-and-get-out property companies that did so well before the Rachman scandal. Naturally, they had made a shoddy job of it: the fittings were cheap and the finish awful; the window frames seemed too small for the brickwork around them, and there were large, rough gaps at every joint. But we had sanded the floors and painted the place out in bright colors. Then we bought bits and pieces from the junk furniture dealers in Chalk Farm, and sanded and painted them, too. So in the end it seemed gay enough in a fragile, skin-deep way: just the place for the first baby, the first book, the first real unhappiness. By the time we left, eighteen months later, there were gaping cracks in the outer wall where the new windows had been cut. But by that time there were gaping cracks in our lives, too, so it all seemed to fit.

Since I was the regular poetry critic for *The Observer*, I saw few writers. To know whom I was reviewing seemed to make too many difficulties: nice men often write bad verse and good poets can be monsters; more often than not both the man and his work were unspeakable. It seemed easier all round not to be able to put a face to the name, and to judge solely by the printed page. I kept to my rule even when I was told that Ted Hughes was living nearby, just across Primrose Hill, with an American wife and a small baby. Three years before he had brought out *The Hawk in the Rain,* which I admired greatly. But there was something about the poems that made me suspect that he wouldn't care what I thought. They seemed to emerge from an absorbed, physical world that was wholly his own; for all the technical skill deployed, they gave the impression that literary goings-on were no concern of the author. "Don't worry," I was told, "he never talks shop." I was also told that he had a wife called Sylvia, who also wrote poetry, "but"—and this was said reassuringly—"she's very sharp and intelligent."

In 1960 came *Lupercal.* I thought it the best book by a young poet that I had read since I began my stint on *The Observer.* When I wrote a review to say so, the paper asked for a short piece about him for one of the more gossipy pages. I phoned him and we arranged to take our kids for a walk on Primrose Hill. It seemed like a nice, neutral idea.

They were living in a tiny flat not far from the Regent's Park Zoo. Their windows faced onto a run-down square: peeling houses around a scrappy wilderness of garden. Closer to the Hill, gentility was advancing fast: smart Sunday newspaper house-agents had their boards up, the front doors were all fashionable colors—"Cantaloupe," "Tangerine," "Blueberry," "Thames Green"—and everywhere was a sense of gleaming white interiors, the old houses writ large and rich with new conversions.

Their square, however, had not yet been taken over. It was dirty, cracked, and racketty with children. The rows of houses that led off it were still occupied by the same kind of working-class families they had been built for eighty years before. No one, as yet, had made them chic and quadrupled their price—though that was to come soon enough. The Hughes' flat was one floor up a bedraggled staircase, past a pram in the hall and a bicycle. It was so small that everything seemed sideways on. You inserted yourself into a hallway so narrow and jammed that you could scarcely take off your coat. The kitchen seemed to fit one person at a time, who could span it with arms outstretched. In the living room you sat side by side, longways on, between a wall of books and a wall of pictures. The bedroom off it, with its flowered wallpaper, seemed to have room for nothing except a double bed. But the colors were cheerful, the bits and pieces pretty, and the whole place had a sense of liveliness about it, of things being done. A typewriter stood on a little table by the window, and they took turns at it, each working shifts while the other minded the baby. At night they cleared it away to make room for the child's cot. Later, they borrowed a room from another American poet, W. S. Merwin, where Sylvia worked the morning shift, Ted the afternoon.

THIS WAS Ted's time. He was on the edge of a considerable reputation. His first book had been well received and won all sorts of prizes in the States, which usually means that the second book will be an anticlimax. Instead, *Lupercal* effortlessly fulfilled and surpassed all the promises of *The Hawk in the Rain*. A figure had emerged on the drab scene of British poetry, powerful and undeniable. Whatever his natural hesitations and distrust of his own work, he must have had some sense of his own strength and achievement. God alone knew how far he was eventually going, but in one essential way he had already arrived. He was a tall, strong-looking man in a black corduroy jacket, black trousers, black shoes; his dark hair hung untidily forward; he had a long, witty mouth. He was in command.

In those days Sylvia seemed effaced; the poet taking a back seat to the young mother and housewife. She had a long, rather flat body, a longish face, not pretty but alert and full of feeling, with a lively mouth and fine brown eyes. Her brownish hair was scraped severely into a bun. She wore jeans and a neat shirt, briskly American: bright, clean, competent, like a young woman in a cookery advertisement, friendly and yet rather distant.

Her background, of which I knew nothing then, belied her housewifely air: she had been a child prodigy—her first poem was published when she was eight—and then a brilliant student, winning every prize to be had, first at Wellesley High School, then at Smith College: scholarships all the way, straight A's, Phi Beta Kappa, president of this and that college society, and prizes for everything. A New York glossy magazine, *Mademoiselle,* had picked her as an outstanding possibility and wined her, dined her, and photographed her all over Manhattan. Then, almost inevitably, she had won a Fulbright to Cambridge, where she met Ted Hughes. They were married in 1956, on Bloomsday. Behind Sylvia was a self-sacrificing, widowed mother, a schoolteacher who had worked herself into the ground so that her two children might flourish. Sylvia's father—ornithologist, entomologist, ichthyologist, international authority on bumblebees, and professor of biology at Boston University—had died when she was nine. Both parents were of German stock and were German-speaking, academic, and intellectual. When she and Ted went to the States after Cambridge, a glittering university career seemed both natural and assured.

On the surface it was a typical success story: the brilliant examination-passer driving forward so fast and relentlessly that nothing could ever catch up with her. And it can last a lifetime, provided nothing checks the momentum, and the vehicle of all those triumphs doesn't disintegrate into sharp fragments from sheer speed and pressure. But already her progress had twice lurched to a halt. Between her month on *Mademoiselle* and her last year in college she had had the nervous breakdown and suicide attempt which became the theme of her novel, *The Bell Jar.* Then, once reestablished at Smith—"an outstanding teacher," said her colleagues—the academic prizes no longer seemed worth the effort. So in 1958 she had thrown over university life—Ted had never seriously contemplated it—and gone freelance, trusting her luck and talent as a poet. All this I learned much later. Now Sylvia had simply slowed down; she was subdued, absorbed in her new baby daughter, and friendly only in that rather formal, shallow, transatlantic way that keeps you at your distance.

Ted went downstairs to get the pram ready while she dressed the baby. I stayed behind a minute, zipping up my son's coat. Sylvia turned to me, suddenly without gush:

"I'm so glad you picked *that* poem," she said. "It's one of my favorites but no one else seemed to like it."

For a moment I went completely blank; I didn't know what she was talking about. She noticed and helped me out.

"The one you put in *The Observer* a year ago. About the factory at night."

"For Christ's sake, Sylvia *Plath*." It was my turn to gush. "I'm sorry. It was a lovely poem."

"Lovely" wasn't the right word, but what else do you say to a bright young housewife? I had picked it from a sheaf of poems which had arrived from America, immaculately typed, with self-addressed envelope and international reply coupon efficiently supplied. All of them were stylish and talented but that in itself was not rare in those days. The late fifties was a period of particularly high style in American verse, when every campus worth its name had its own "brilliant" poetic technician in residence. But at least one of these poems had more going for it than rhetorical elegance. It had no title, though later, in *The Colossus,* she called it "Night Shift." It was one of those poems which starts by saying what it is *not* about so strongly that you don't believe the explanations that follow:

> It was not a heart, beating,
> That muted boom, that clangor
> Far off, not blood in the ears
> Drumming up any fever
>
> To impose on the evening.
> The noise came from outside:
> A metal detonating
> Native, evidently, to
>
> These stilled suburbs: nobody
> Startled at it, though the sound
> Shook the ground with its pounding.
> It took root at my coming . . .

It seemed to me more than a piece of good description, to be used and moralized upon as the fashion of that decade dictated. The note was aroused and all the details of the scene seemed continually to be turning inward. It is a poem, I suppose, about fear, and although in the course of it the fear is rationalized and explained (that pounding in the night is caused by machines turning), it ends by reasserting precisely the threatening masculine forces there were to be afraid of. It had its moments of awkwardness—for example, the prissy, pausing flourish in the manner of Wallace Stevens: "Native, evidently, to . . ." But compared with most of the stuff that thudded unsolicited through my letterbox every morning, it was that rare thing: the always unexpected, wholly genuine article.

I was embarrassed not to have known who she was. She seemed embarrassed to have reminded me, and also depressed.

AFTER THAT I saw Ted occasionally, Sylvia more rarely. He and I would meet for a beer in one of the pubs near Primrose Hill or the Heath, and sometimes we would walk our children together. We almost never talked shop; without mentioning it, we wanted to keep things unprofessional. At some point during the summer Ted and I did a broadcast together. Afterward we collected Sylvia from the flat and went across to their local. The recording had been a success and we stood outside the pub, around the baby's pram, drinking our beers and pleased with ourselves. Sylvia, too, seemed easier, wittier, less constrained than I had seen her before. For the first time I understood something of the real charm and speed of the girl.

About that time my wife and I moved from our flat near Swiss Cottage to a house higher up in Hampstead, near the Heath. A couple of days before we were due to move I broke my leg in a climbing accident, and that put out everything and everyone, since the house had to be decorated, broken leg or not. I remember sticking black and white tiles to floor after endless floor, a filthy dark brown glue coating my fingers and clothes and gumming up my hair, the great, inert plaster cast dragging behind me like a coffin as I crawled. There wasn't much time for friends. Ted occasionally dropped in and I would hobble with him briefly to the pub. But I saw Sylvia not at all. In the autumn I went to teach for a term in the States.

While I was there *The Observer* sent me her first book of poems to review. It seemed to fit the image I had of her: serious, gifted, withheld, and still partly under the massive shadow of her husband. There were poems that had been influenced by him, others which echoed Theodore

Roethke or Wallace Stevens; clearly, she was still casting about for her own style. Yet the technical ability was great, and beneath most of the poems was a sense of resources and disturbances not yet tapped. "Her poems," I wrote, "rest secure in a mass of experience that is never quite brought out into the daylight. . . . It is this sense of threat, as though she were continually menaced by something she could see only out of the corners of her eyes, that gives her work its distinction."

I still stand by that judgment. In the light of her subsequent work and, more persuasively, her subsequent death, *The Colossus* has been overrated. "Anyone can see," the doctrine now runs, "that it's all there in crystalline form." There are even academic critics who prefer these elegant early poems to the more naked and brutal frontal attacks of her mature work, although when the book first appeared their reviews were cool enough. Meanwhile, hindsight can alter the historical importance but not the quality of the verse. *The Colossus* established her credentials: it contained a handful of beautiful poems, but more important was the sheer ability of the work, the precision and concentration with which she handled language, the unemphatic range of vocabulary, her ear for subtle rhythms, and her assurance in handling and subduing rhymes and half-rhymes. Obviously, she had now developed the craft to cope with anything that arrived. My mistake was to imply that at that stage she hadn't, or wouldn't, recognize the forces that shook her. It turned out that she knew them all too well: they had driven her to the thin near edge of suicide when she was nineteen, and already in the last piece in the book, the long "Poem for a Birthday," she was turning to face them. But the echoes of Roethke in the poem obscured that for me, and I couldn't see it.

When I got back from the States in February, 1961, I saw the Hugheses again, but briefly and not often. Ted had fallen out of love with London and was fretting to get away; Sylvia had been ill—first a miscarriage, then appendicitis—and I had my own problems, a divorce. I remember her thanking me for the review of *The Colossus*, adding disarmingly that she agreed with the qualifications. I also remember her enthusing about the beautiful house they had found in Devon—old, thatched, flagstoned, and with a large orchard. They moved, I moved, something was finished.

Both of them continued to send poems to *The Observer*. In May, 1961, we published Sylvia's poem about her daughter, "Morning Song"; in November of that year, "Mojave Desert," which has not yet been collected; two months later, "The Rival." The current was deepening, its flow becoming easier.

I DIDN'T SEE her again until June, 1962, when I dropped in on them on my way down to Cornwall for the long Whitsun weekend. They were living a few miles north of Exeter. By Devon standards it wasn't a pretty village: more gray stone and gloom than timber, thatch, and flowers. Where the most perfect English villages give the impression of never having been properly awakened, theirs seemed to have retired into sleep. Once it might have been a center for the surrounding countryside, a place of some presence where things happened. But not any more. Exeter had taken over, and the life of this village had drained slowly away, like a family that has come down in the world.

The Hughes' house had once been the local manor. It was set slightly above the rest of the village, up a steep lane next to a twelfth-century church, and seemed important. It was large and thatched, the walls and passages were stone, the rooms gleamed with new paint. We sat out in the big wild garden drinking tea while little Frieda, now aged two, teetered among the flowers. There was a small army of apple and cherry trees, a vivid laburnum swaying with blossom, a vegetable patch, and, off to one side, a little hillock. It turned out to be a prehistoric burial mound. Given the Hughes' flair and tastes, it could hardly have been anything else. Flowers glowed everywhere, the grass was long and unkempt, and the whole luxuriant place seemed to be overflowing with summer.

They had had a new baby in January, a boy, and Sylvia had changed. No longer quiet and withheld, a housewifely appendage to a powerful husband, she seemed made solid and complete, her own woman again. Perhaps the birth of a son had something to do with this new confident air. But there was a sharpness and clarity about her that seemed to go beyond that. It was she who showed me round the house and the garden; the electric gadgets, the freshly painted rooms, the orchard and the burial mound—above all, the burial mound, "the wall of old corpses," she called it later in a poem—were *her* property. Ted, meanwhile, seemed content to sit back and play with little Frieda, who clung to him dependently. Since it was a strong, close marriage, he seemed unconcerned that the balance of power had shifted for the time being to her.

I understood why as I was leaving. "I'm writing again," she said. "Really writing. I'd like you to see some of the new poems." Her manner was warm and open, as though she had decided I could be trusted.

Some time before, *The Observer* had accepted a poem by her called "Finisterre." We finally published it that August. In the meantime she sent a beautiful short poem, "Crossing the Water," which is not in *Ariel*, although it is as good as many that are. It arrived with a formal note and a meticulously stamped, self-addressed envelope. She seemed to be functioning as efficiently as ever. Yet when I saw Ted sometime later in London, he was tense and preoccupied. Driving on her own, Sylvia had had an accident, hurting herself and smashing up their old Morris station wagon. It could have meant anything but I judged it was serious, if only from the way his dark presence, as he spoke, darkened an even deeper shade of gloom.

WHEN AUGUST came I went abroad for a few weeks, and by the time I got back autumn had already started. Although it was not yet mid-September, the leaves had begun to blow about the streets and the rain came down. That first morning, when I woke up to a drowning London sky, summer seemed as far away as the Mediterranean itself. Automatically, I found myself huddling into my clothes: the London crouch. We were in for a long winter.

At the end of September *The Observer* published "Crossing the Water." One afternoon soon after, when I

was working and the charlady was banging around upstairs, the bell rang. It was Sylvia, smartly dressed, determinedly bright and cheerful.

"I was just passing, so I thought I'd drop in," she said.
With her formal town clothes and prim bun of hair, she
had the air of an Edwardian lady performing a delicate
but necessary social duty.

The little studio I rented had been converted from an
old stable. It lay down a long passage, behind a garage,
and was beautiful, in its crumbling way, but uncomfortable: there was nothing to lounge on—only spidery Windsor
chairs and a couple of rugs on the blood-red uncarpeted
lino. I poured her a drink and she settled in front of the
coal stove on one of the rugs, like a student, very much at
her ease, sipping whiskey and making the ice clink in her
glass.

"That sound makes me homesick for the States," she said.
"It's the only thing that does."

We talked about her poem in *The Observer*, then chatted
about nothing in particular. Finally, I asked her why she
was in town. She replied, with a kind of polished cheerfulness, that she was flat-hunting, and then added casually
that she and the children were living on their own for the
time being. I remembered the last time I had seen her, in
that overflowing Devon garden, and it seemed impossible
that anything could have disrupted the idyll. But I asked
no questions and she offered no explanations. Instead, she
began to talk about the new drive to write that was upon
her. At least a poem a day, she said, and often more. She
made it sound like demonic possession. And it occurred to
me that maybe this was why she and her husband had,
however temporarily, parted: it was a question not of differences but of intolerable similarities. When two genuinely
original, ambitious, full-time poets join in one marriage,
and both are productive, every poem one writes must feel
to the other as though it had been dug out of his, or her,
own skull. At a certain pitch of creative intensity it must
be more unbearable for the Muse to be unfaithful to you
with your partner than for him, or her, to betray you with
a whole army of seducers.

"I'd like to read you some of the new poems," she said,

and pulled a sheaf of typescripts from her shoulder-bag on the floor beside her.

"Gladly," I said, reaching over for them. "Let's see."

She shook her head: "No. I don't want you to read them to yourself. They've got to be read out loud. I want you to *hear* them."

So, sitting cross-legged on the uncomfortable floor, with the charlady clanking away upstairs, she read me "Berck-Plage":

This is the sea, then, this great abeyance . . .

She read fast, in a hard, slightly nasal accent, rapping it out as though she were angry. Even now I find it a difficult poem to follow, the development indirect, the images concentrated and eliding thickly together. I had a vague impression of something injurious and faintly obscene, but I don't think I understood much. So when she finished I asked her to read it again. This time I heard it a little more clearly and could make some remarks about details. In some way, this seemed to satisfy her. We argued a bit and she read me more poems: one of them was "The Moon and the Yew Tree"; "Elm," I think, was another; there were six or eight in all. She would let me read none to myself, so I didn't get much, if anything, of their subtlety. But I did at least recognize that I was hearing something strong and new and hard to come to terms with. I suppose I picked on whatever details and slight signs of weakness I could as a kind of protection. She, in her turn, seemed happy to read, argue, and be heard sympathetically.

"She's a poet, isn't she?" asked my charlady the next day.

"Yes."

"I thought so," she said with grim satisfaction.

AFTER THAT, Sylvia dropped in fairly often on her visits to London, always with a batch of new poems to read. This way I first heard, among others, the "Bee" poems, "A Birthday Present," "The Applicant," "Getting There," "Fever 103°," "Letter in November," and "Ariel," which I thought extraordinary. I told her it was the best thing she had done, and a few days later she sent me a fair copy of it, carefully written out in her heavy, rounded script, and illuminated like a medieval manuscript with flowers and ornamental squiggles.

One day—I'm not sure when—she read me what she called "some light verse." She meant "Daddy" and "Lady Lazarus." Her voice, as she read them, was hot and full of venom. By this time I could hear the poetry fairly clearly, without too great a time-lag and sense of inadequacy. I was appalled; at first hearing, the things seemed to be not so much poetry as assault and battery. And because I now knew something about her life, there was no avoiding how much she was part of the action. But to have commented on that would have been to imply that the poems had failed as poetry, which they clearly had not. As always, my defense was to nag her about details. There was one line I picked on in particular:

Gentlemen, ladies

These are my hands
My knees.
I may be skin and bone,
I may be Japanese . . .

"Why *Japanese?*" I niggled away at her, "Do you just need the rhyme? Or are you trying to hitch an easy lift by dragging in the atomic victims? If you're going to use this kind of violent material, you've got to play it cool . . ." She argued back sharply but later, when the poem was finally published after her death, the line had gone. And that, I think, is a pity: she did need the rhyme; the tone is quite controlled enough to support the apparently not quite relevant allusion; and I was overreacting to the initial brutality of the verse without understanding its weird elegance.

Throughout this time the evidence of the poems and the evidence of the person were utterly different. There was no trace of the poetry's despair and unforgiving destructiveness in her social manner. She remained remorselessly bright and energetic: busy with her children and her bee-keeping in Devon, busy flat-hunting in London, busy seeing *The Bell Jar* through the press, busy typing and sending

off her poems to largely unreceptive editors (just before
she died she sent a sheaf of her best poems, most of them
now classics, to one of the national British weeklies; none
was accepted). She had also taken up horse-riding again,
teaching herself to ride on a powerful stallion called Ariel,
and was elated by this new excitement.

Cross-legged on the red floor, after reading her poems,
she would talk about her riding in her twanging New England voice. And perhaps because I was also a member of
the club, she talked, too, about suicide in much the same
way: about her attempt ten years before which, I suppose,
must have been very much on her mind as she corrected
the proofs of her novel, and about her recent car crash.
It had been no accident; she had gone off the road deliberately, seriously, wanting to die. But she hadn't, and all
that was now in the past. For this reason I am convinced
that at this time she was not contemplating suicide. On
the contrary, she was able to write about the act so freely
because it was already behind her. The car crash was a
death she had survived, the death she sardonically felt herself fated to undergo once every decade:

> I have done it again.
> One year in every ten
> I manage it—
>
> A sort of walking miracle . . .
> I am only thirty.
> And like the cat I have nine times to die.
>
> This is Number Three . . .

In life, as in the poem, there was neither hysteria in her
voice, nor any appeal for sympathy. She talked about suicide in much the same tone as she talked about any other
risky, testing activity: urgently, even fiercely, but altogether without self-pity. She seemed to view death as a
physical challenge she had, once again, overcome. It was
an experience of much the same quality as riding Ariel or
mastering a bolting horse—which she had done as a Cambridge undergraduate—or careening down a dangerous

snow slope without properly knowing how to ski—an inci-
dent, also from life, which is one of the best things in *The
Bell Jar.* Suicide, in short, was not a swoon into death, an
attempt "to cease upon the midnight with no pain"; it was
something to be felt in the nerve-ends and fought against,
an initiation rite qualifying her for a *life* of her own.

God knows what wound the death of her father had
inflicted on her in her childhood, but over the years this
had been transformed into the conviction that to be an
adult meant to be a survivor. So, for her, death was a
debt to be met once every decade: in order to stay alive
as a grown woman, a mother, and a poet, she had to pay—
in some partial, magical way—with her life. But because
this impossible payment involved also the fantasy of join-
ing or regaining her beloved dead father, it was a passionate act, instinct as much with love as with hatred and
despair. Thus in that strange, upsetting poem "The Bee
Meeting," the detailed, doubtless accurate description of a
gathering of local beekeepers in her Devon village gradually becomes an invocation of some deadly ritual in which
she is the sacrificial virgin whose coffin, finally, waits in the
sacred grove. Why this should happen becomes, perhaps,
slightly less mysterious when you remember that her father
was an authority on bees; so her beekeeping becomes a way
of symbolically allying herself to him, and reclaiming him
from the dead.

THE TONE of all these late poems is hard, factual and,
despite the intensity, understated. In some strange way,
I suspect she thought of herself as a realist: the deaths
and resurrections of "Lady Lazarus," the nightmares of
"Daddy" and the rest had all been proved on her pulses.
That she brought to them an extraordinary inner wealth
of imagery and associations was almost beside the point,
however essential it is for the poetry itself. Because she
felt she was simply describing the facts as they had happened, she was able to tap in the coolest possible way all
her large reserves of skill: those subtle rhymes and half-
rhymes, the flexible, echoing rhythms and offhand collo-
quialism by which she preserved, even in her most an-
guished probing, complete artistic control. Her internal

horrors were as factual and precisely sensed as the barely controllable stallion on which she was learning to ride or the car she had smashed up.

So she spoke of suicide with a wry detachment, and without any mention of the suffering or drama of the act. It was obviously a matter of self-respect that her first attempt had been serious and nearly successful, instead of a mere hysterical gesture. That seemed to entitle her to speak of suicide as a subject, not as an obsession. It was an act she felt she had a right to as a grown woman and a free agent, in the same way as she felt it to be necessary to her development, given her queer conception of the adult as a survivor, an imaginary Jew from the concentration camps of the mind. Because of this there was never any question of motives: you do it because you do it, just as an artist always knows what he knows.

Perhaps this is why she scarcely mentioned her father, however clearly and deeply her fantasies of death were involved with him. The autobiographical heroine of *The Bell Jar* goes to weep at her father's grave immediately before she holes up in a cellar and swallows fifty sleeping pills. In "Daddy," describing the same episode, she hammers home her reasons with repetitions:

> At twenty I tried to die
> And get back, back, back to you.
> I thought even the bones would do.

I suspect that finding herself alone again now, however temporarily and voluntarily, all the anguish she had experienced at her father's death was reactivated: despite herself, she felt abandoned, injured, enraged, and bereaved as purely and defenselessly as she had as a child twenty years before. As a result, the pain that had built up steadily inside her all that time came flooding out. There was no need to discuss motives because the poems did that for her.

These months were an amazingly creative period, comparable, I think, to the "marvellous year" in which Keats produced nearly all the poetry on which his reputation finally rests. Earlier she had written carefully, more or less painfully, with much rewriting and, according to her husband, with constant recourse to *Roget's Thesaurus*. Now, although she abandoned none of her hard-earned skills and discipline, and still rewrote and rewrote, the poems flowed effortlessly, until, at the end, she occasionally produced as many as three a day. She also told me that she was deep into a new novel. *The Bell Jar* was finished, proofread and with her publishers; she spoke of it with some embarrassment as an autobiographical apprentice-work which she had to write in order to free herself from the past. But this new book, she implied, was the genuine article.

Considering the conditions in which she worked, her productivity was phenomenal. She was a full-time mother with a two-year-old daughter, a baby of ten months, and a house to look after. By the time the children were in bed at night she was too tired for anything more strenuous than "music and brandy and water." So she got up very early each morning and worked until the children woke. "These new poems of mine have one thing in common," she wrote in a note for a reading she prepared, but never broadcast, for the BBC, "they were all written at about four in the morning—that still blue, almost eternal hour before the baby's cry, before the glassy music of the milkman, settling his bottles." In those dead hours between night and day, she was able to gather herself into herself in silence and isolation, almost as though she were reclaiming some past innocence and freedom before life got a grip on her. Then she could write. For the rest of the day she was shared among the children, the housework, the shopping, efficient, bustling, harassed, like every other housewife.

BUT THIS DAWN SENSE of paradise temporarily regained does not explain the sudden flowering and change in her work. Technically, the clue is in her insistence that she herself should always read the poems out loud. In the early sixties this was a rare procedure. It was, after all, still a period of high formalism, of Stevensesque cadences and Empsonian ambiguities at which she herself was, as her earlier work proved, particularly adept. Essentially, this was the style of the academies, of self-imposed limitations of feeling and narrow devotion to the duties of craftsmanship which were echoed in thumping iambics and painfully analyzable imagery. But in 1958 she had made the vital decision to abandon the university career for which she had so carefully prepared herself all through her adolescence and early twenties. Only gradually over the next four years did that total commitment to her own creative life emerge in the fabric of her verse, breaking down the old, inert molds, quickening the rhythms, broadening the emotional range. The decision to abandon teaching was the first critical step toward achieving her identity as a poet, just as the birth of her children seemed, as she described it, to vindicate her as a woman. In these last poems the process was complete: the poet and the poems became one. What she wrote depended on her voice in the same way as her children depended on her love.

The other crucial element in her poetic maturity was the example of Robert Lowell's *Life Studies*. I say "example" rather than "influence" because, although Sylvia had attended Lowell's classes at Boston University in the company of Anne Sexton and George Starbuck, she never picked up his peculiarly contagious style. Instead of a style, she took from him a freedom. She told a British Council interviewer:

> I've been very excited by what I feel is the new breakthrough that came with, say, Robert Lowell's *Life Studies*. This intense breakthrough into very serious, very personal emotional experience, which I feel has been partly taboo. Robert Lowell's poems about his experiences in a mental hospital, for example, interest me very much. These peculiar private and taboo subjects I feel have been explored in recent American poetry . . .

Lowell provided her with an example of the quality she most admired outside poetry and had herself in profusion: courage. In its way, *Life Studies* was as brave and revolutionary as *The Waste Land*. After all, it appeared at the height of the tight-lipped fifties, the era of doctrinaire New Criticism, of the Intentional Fallacy, and the whole elaborate, iron dogma by which poetry was separated utterly from the man who made it. In his time, Lowell had been the darling of the school with his complex Catholic symbolism, thickly textured Eliot-Elizabethan language, and his unwavering ability to stamp every line with his own individual rhythm. Then, after nearly ten years' silence, he turned his back on it all. The symbols disappeared, the language clarified and became colloquial, the subject matter became intensely, insistently personal. He wrote as a man who had had breakdowns and was haunted at every crisis by family ghosts; and he wrote without evasions. All that was left of the former young master of Alexandrian complexity was the still unanswerable skill and originality. Even more strongly than before, it was impossible to avoid the troubled presence of Lowell himself, but now he was speaking out in a way that violated all the principles of New Criticism: there was immediacy instead of impersonality, vulnerability in place of exquisitely dandified irony.

Sylvia derived from all this, above all, a vast sense of release. It was as though Lowell had opened a door which had previously been bolted against her. At a critical moment in her development there was no longer any need to be imprisoned in her old poetic habits which despite their elegance—or maybe because of it—she now felt to be intolerably constricting. "My first book, *The Colossus*"—she told the man from the British Council—"I can't read any of the poems aloud now. I didn't write them to be read aloud. In fact, they quite privately bore me." *The Colossus* was the culmination of her apprenticeship in the craft of poetry; it completed the training she began as an eight-year-old and continued through the tensely stylish verse of her undergraduate days, when each poem seemed built up grudgingly, word by word, like a mosaic. Now all that was behind her. She had outgrown the style; more important, she had outgrown the person who had written in that oblique, reticent way. A combination of forces, some chosen deliberately, others chosen for her, had brought her to the point where she was able to write as from her true center about the forces that really moved her: destructive, volatile, demanding, a world apart from everything she had been trained to admire. "What," asked Coleridge, "is the height and ideal of mere association? Delirium." For years Sylvia had apparently agreed, pursuing formal virtues and fingertip detachment, contemptuous of the self-pity, self-advertisement, and self-indulgence of the Beatniks. Now, right on cue, came *Life Studies* to prove that the violence of the self could be written about with control, subtlety, and a dispassionate but undefended imagination.

I suspect that this is why she had first come to me with the new poems, although she knew me only glancingly. It helped that I had reviewed *The Colossus* sympathetically and had got *The Observer* to publish some of her more recent things. But more important was the introduction to my Penguin anthology, *The New Poetry*, which had been published the previous spring. In it I had attacked the British poets' nervous preference for gentility above all else, and their avoidance of the uncomfortable, destructive truths both of the inner life and of the present time. Apparently, this essay said something she wanted to hear; she spoke of it often and with approval, and was disappointed not to have been included among the poets in the book. (She was, later, since her work, more than anyone else's, vindicates my argument. But in the first edition I had stuck to British poets, with the exception of two older Americans, Lowell and Berryman, who, I felt, set the tone for the postwar, post-Eliot period.) Perhaps it made things easier for her to know that someone was making a critical case for what she was now trying to do. And perhaps it made her feel less lonely.

YET LONELY SHE WAS, touchingly and without much disguise, despite her buoyant manner. Despite, too, the energy of her poems, which are, by any standards, subtly ambiguous performances. In them she faced her private horrors steadily and without looking aside, but the effort and risk involved in doing so acted on her like a stimulant; the worse things got and the more directly she wrote about them, the more fertile her imagination became. Just as disaster, when it finally arrives, is never as bad as it seems in expectation, so she now wrote almost with relief, swiftly as though to forestall further horrors. In a way, this is what she had been waiting for all her life, and now it had come she knew she must use it. "The passion for destruction is also a creative passion," said Michael Bakunin, and for

Sylvia also this was true. She turned anger, implacability, and her roused, needle-sharp sense of trouble into a kind of celebration.

I have suggested that her cool tone depends a great deal on her realism, her sense of fact. As the months went by and her poetry became progressively more extreme, this gift of transforming every detail grew steadily until, in the last weeks, each trivial event became the occasion for poetry: a cut finger, a fever, a bruise. Her drab domestic life fused with her imagination richly and without hesitation. Around this time, for example, her husband produced a strange radio play in which the hero, driving to town, runs over a hare, sells the dead animal for five shillings, and with the blood money buys two roses. Sylvia pounced on this, isolating its core, interpreting and adjusting it according to her own needs. The result was the poem "Kindness," which ends:

> The blood jet is poetry,
> There is no stopping it.
> You hand me two children, two roses.

There was, indeed, no stopping it. Her poetry acted as a strange, powerful lens through which her ordinary life was filtered and refigured with extraordinary intensity. Perhaps the elation that comes of writing well and often helped her to preserve that bright American façade she unfailingly presented to the world. In common with her other friends of that period, I chose to believe in this cheerfulness against all the evidence of the poems. Or rather, I believed in it, and I didn't believe. But what could one do? I felt sorry for her but she clearly didn't want that. Her jauntiness forestalled all sympathy, and, if only by her blank refusal to discuss them otherwise, she insisted that her poems were purely poems, autonomous. If attempted suicide is, as some psychiatrists believe, a cry for help, then Sylvia at this time was not suicidal. What she wanted was not help but confirmation: she needed someone to acknowledge that she was coping exceptionally well with her difficult routine life of children, nappies, shopping, and writing. She needed, even more, to know that the poems worked and were good, for although she had gone through a gate Lowell had opened, she was now far along a peculiarly solitary road on which not many would risk following her. So it was important for her to know that her messages were coming back clear and strong. Yet not even her determinedly bright self-reliance could disguise the loneliness that came from her almost palpably, like a heat haze. She asked for neither sympathy nor help but, like a bereaved widow at a wake, she simply wanted company in her mourning. I suppose it provided confirmation that, despite the odds and the internal evidence, she still existed.

ONE GLOOMY November afternoon she arrived at my studio greatly excited. As usual, she had been trudging the chill streets, house-hunting despondently and more or less aimlessly. A block away from the square near Primrose Hill where she and Ted had lived when they first came to London she saw a "To Let" notice up in front of a newly refurbished house. That in itself was something of a miracle in those impossible, overcrowded days. But more important, the house bore a blue plaque announcing that Yeats had once lived there. It was a sign, the confirmation she had been looking for. That summer she had visited Yeats' Tower at Ballylea and wrote to a friend that she thought it "the most beautiful and peaceful place in the world"; now there was a possibility of finding another Yeats tower in her favorite part of London which she could in some way share with the great poet. She hurried to the agent's and found, improbably, that she was the first to apply. Another sign. On the spot she took a five-year lease of the flat, although the rent was more than she could afford. Then she walked across dark, blowy Primrose Hill to tell me the news.

She was elated not just because she had at last found a flat but because the place and its associations seemed to her somehow preordained. In varying degrees, both she and her husband seemed to believe in the occult. As artists, I suppose, they had to, since both were intent on finding voices for their unquiet, buried selves. But there was, I think, something more to their belief than that. Ted has written that "her psychic gifts, at almost any time, were strong enough to make her frequently wish to be rid of them." That could simply have been her poet's knack of sensing the unspoken content of every situation and, later, her easy, instinctive access to her own unconscious. Yet although both of them talked often enough about astrology, dreams, and magic—enough, anyway, to imply that this was not just a casually interesting subject—I had the impression that at heart their attitudes were utterly different. Ted constantly and carefully mocked himself and deflated his pretensions, yet there was always a sense of his being in touch with some primitive area, some dark side of the self which had nothing to do with the young literary man. This, after all, was what his poems were about: an immediate, physical apprehension of the violence both of animal life and of the self—of the animality of the self. It was also part of his physical presence, a quality of threat beneath his shrewd, laconic manner. It was almost as though, despite all the reading and polish and craftsmanship, he had never properly been civilized or had, at least, never properly believed in his civilization. It was simply a shell he sardonically put up with for the sake of convenience. So all that astrology, primitive religion, and black magic he talked about, however ironically, was a kind of metaphor for the shaking but obscure creative powers he knew himself to possess. For this reason those dubious topics took on for him an immediacy which may not have implied any belief but which certainly transformed them into something beyond mere fad. Perhaps all I am describing is, quite simply, a touch of genius. But it is a genius that has little to do with the traditional Romantic concept of the word: with Shelley's canny other-worldliness or Byron's equally canny sense of his own drama. Ted, too, is canny and practical, like most Yorkshiremen, unwillingly fooled and with a fine, racing mechanic's ear for the rumblings of the literary machine. But he is also, in a curiously complete way, an original: his reactions are unpredictable, his frame of reference different. I imagine the most extreme example of this style of genius was Blake. But there are also many people of genius—perhaps the majority—who have almost nothing of that dislocating and dislocated quality: T. S. Eliot, for example, the Polish poet Zbigniew Herbert, John Donne and Keats—all men whose unusual creative intelligence and awareness seem not essentially at odds with the reality of their everyday worlds. Instead, their particular gift is to clarify and intensify the received world.

Sylvia, I think, belonged with these latter. Her intensity was of the nerves, something urban and near screaming-point. It was also, in its way, more intellectual than Ted's. It was part of the fierceness with which she had worked as a student, passing exam after exam brilliantly, easily, hungrily. With the same intensity she immersed herself in her children, her riding, her beekeeping, even her cooking; everything had to be done well and to the fullest. Since her husband was interested in the occult—for whatever clouded personal reasons—she threw herself into that, too, almost out of the desire to excel. And because her natural talents were very great, she discovered she had "psychic gifts." No doubt the results were genuine and even uncanny, but I suspect they were a triumph of mind over ectoplasm. It is the same in the poems: Ted's gain their effect by expressing his sense of menace and violence immediately, unanswerably; in Sylvia's the expression, though often more powerful, is a by-product of a compulsive need to understand.

On Christmas Eve, 1962, Sylvia telephoned me: she and the children had finally settled into their new apartment; could I come round that evening to see the place, have a meal, and hear some new poems? As it happened, I couldn't, since I had already been invited to dinner by some friends who lived a few streets away from her. I said I'd drop in for a drink on my way.

She seemed different. Her hair, which she usually wore in a tight, schoolmistressy bun, was loose. It hung straight to her waist like a tent, giving her pale face and gaunt figure a curiously desolate, rapt air, like a priestess emptied out by the rites of her cult. When she walked in front of me down the hall passage and up the stairs to her apartment—she had the top two floors of the house—her hair gave off a strong smell, sharp as an animal's. The children were already in bed upstairs and the flat was silent. It was newly painted, white and chill. There were, as I remember, no curtains up yet, and the night pressed in coldly on the windows. She had deliberately kept the place bare: rush matting on the floor, a few books, bits of Victoriana, and cloudy blue glass on the shelves, a couple of small Leonard Baskin woodcuts. It was rather beautiful, in its chaste, stripped-down way, but cold, very cold, and the oddments of flimsy Christmas decoration made it seem doubly forlorn, each seeming to repeat that she and the children would be alone over Christmas. For the unhappy, Christmas is always a bad time: the terrible false jollity that comes at you from every side, braying about goodwill and peace and family fun, makes loneliness and depression particularly hard to bear. I had never seen her so strained.

We drank wine and, as usual, she read me some poems. One of them was "Death & Co." This time there was no escaping the meaning. When she had written about death before, it was as something survived, even surpassed: "Lady Lazarus" ends with a resurrection and a threat, and even in "Daddy" she manages finally to turn her back on the grinning, beckoning figure—"Daddy, daddy, you bastard, I'm through." Hence, perhaps, the energy of these poems, their weird jollity in the teeth of everything, their recklessness. But now, as though poetry really were a form of black magic, the figure she had invoked so often, only to dismiss triumphantly, had risen before her, dank, final, and not to be denied. He appeared to her in both his usual shapes: like her father, elderly, unforgiving, and very dead, and also younger, more seductive, a creature of her own generation and choice.[1] This time there was no way out for her; she could only sit still and pretend they hadn't noticed her:

> I do not stir.
> The frost makes a flower,
> The dew makes a star,

---

[1] In her own note on the poem, which she wrote for the BBC, Sylvia said: "This poem—'Death & Co.'—is about the double or schizophrenic nature of death—the marmoreal coldness of Blake's death mask, say, hand in glove with the fearful softness of worms, water, and other katabolists. I imagine these two aspects of death as two men, two business friends, who have come to call."

The dead bell,
The dead bell.

Somebody's done for.

Perhaps the bell was tolling for "somebody" other than herself; but she didn't seem to believe so.

I didn't know what to say. The earlier poems had all insisted, in their different ways, that she wanted nobody's help—although I suddenly realized that maybe they had insisted in such a manner as to make you understand that help might be acceptable, if you were willing to make the effort. But now she was beyond the reach of anyone. In the beginning she had called up these horrors partly in the hope of exorcising them, partly to demonstrate her omnipotence and invulnerability. Now she was shut in with them and knew she was defenseless.

I remember arguing inanely about the phrase "The nude /Verdigris of the condor." I said it was exaggerated, morbid. On the contrary, she replied, that was exactly how a condor's legs looked. She was right, of course. I was only trying, in a futile way, to reduce the tension and take her mind momentarily off her private horrors—as though that could be done by argument and literary criticism! She must have felt I was stupid and insensitive. Which I was. But to have been otherwise would have meant accepting responsibilities I didn't want and couldn't, in my own depression, have coped with. When I left about eight o'clock to go on to my dinner party, I knew I had let her down in some final and unforgivable way. And I knew she knew. I never again saw her alive.

IT WAS AN unspeakable winter, the worst, they said, in a hundred and fifty years. The snow began just after Christmas and would not let up. By New Year the whole country had ground to a halt. The trains froze on the tracks, the abandoned trucks froze on the roads. The power stations, overloaded by million upon pathetic million of hopeless electric fires, broke down continually; not that the fires mattered, since the electricians were mostly out on strike. Water pipes froze solid; for a bath you had to scheme and cajole those rare friends with centrally heated houses, who became rarer and less friendly as the weeks dragged on. Doing the dishes became a major operation. The gastric rumble of water in outdated plumbing was sweeter than the sound of mandolins. Weight for weight, plumbers were as expensive as smoked salmon, and harder to find. The gas failed and Sunday joints went raw. The lights failed and candles, of course, were unobtainable. Nerves failed and marriages crumbled. Finally, the heart failed. It seemed the cold would never end. Nag, nag, nag.

In December *The Observer* had published a still uncollected poem by Sylvia called "Event"; in mid-January they published another, "Winter Trees." Sylvia wrote me a note about it, adding that maybe we should take our children to the zoo and she would show me "the nude verdigris of the condor." But she no longer dropped into my studio with poems. Later that month I met the literary editor of one of the big weeklies. He asked me if I had seen Sylvia recently.

"No. Why?"

"I was just wondering. She sent us some poems. Very strange."

"Did you like them?"

"No," he replied. "Too extreme for my taste. I sent them all back. But she sounds in a bad state. I think she needs help."

Her doctor, a sensitive, overworked man, thought the same. He prescribed sedatives and arranged for her to see a psychotherapist. Having been bitten once by American psychiatry, she hesitated for some time before writing for an appointment. But her depression did not lift, and finally the letter was sent. It did no good. Either her letter or that of the therapist arranging a consultation went astray; apparently the postman delivered it to the wrong address. The therapist's reply arrived a day or two after she died. This was one of several links in the chain of accidents, coincidences, and mistakes that ended in her death.

I AM CONVINCED by what I know of the facts that this time she did not intend to die. Her suicide attempt ten years before had been, in every sense, deadly serious. She had

carefully disguised the theft of the sleeping pills, left a
misleading note to cover her tracks, and hidden herself in
the darkest, most unused corner of a cellar, rearranging
behind her the old firelogs she had disturbed, burying
herself away like a skeleton in the nethermost family closet.
Then she had swallowed a bottle of fifty sleeping pills.
She was found late and by accident, and survived only by
a miracle. The flow of life in her was too strong even for
the violence she had done it. This, anyway, is her description of the act in *The Bell Jar;* there is no reason to believe
it false. So she had learned the hard way the odds against
successful suicide; she had learned that despair must be
counterpoised by an almost obsessional attention to detail
and disguise.

By these lights she seemed, in her last attempt, to be
taking care not to succeed. But this time everything con-
spired to destroy her. An employment agency had found
her an *au pair* girl to help with the children and housework
while Sylvia got on with her writing. The girl, an Australian,
was due to arrive at nine o'clock on the morning of Monday,
February 11th. Meanwhile, a recurrent trouble, Sylvia's
sinuses were bad; the pipes in her newly converted flat
froze solid; there was still no telephone, and no word from
the psychotherapist; the weather continued monstrous.
Illness, loneliness, depression, and cold, combined with
the demands of two small children, were too much for her.
So when the weekend came she went off with the babies to
stay with friends in another part of London. The plan was,
I think, that she would leave early enough on Monday
morning to be back in time to welcome the Australian girl.
Instead, she decided to go back on the Sunday. The friends
were against it but she was insistent, made a great show
of her old competence and seemed more cheerful than
she had been for some time. So they let her go. About
eleven o'clock that night she knocked on the door of the
elderly painter who lived below her, asking to borrow some
stamps. But she lingered in the doorway, drawing out the
conversation until he told her that he got up well before
nine in the morning. Then she said goodnight and went
back upstairs.

God knows what kind of a sleepless night she spent or

if she wrote any poetry. Certainly, within the last few days
of her life she wrote one of her most beautiful poems,
"Edge," which is specifically about the act she was about
to perform:

> The woman is perfected.
> Her dead
>
> Body wears the smile of accomplishment,
> The illusion of a Greek necessity
>
> Flows in the scrolls of her toga,
> Her bare
>
> Feet seem to be saying:
> We have come so far, it is over.
>
> Each dead child coiled, a white serpent,
> One at each little
>
> Pitcher of milk, now empty.
> She has folded
>
> Them back into her body as petals
> Of a rose close when the garden
>
> Stiffens and odors bleed
> From the sweet, deep throats of the night flowers.
>
> The moon has nothing to be sad about,
> Staring from her hood of bone.
>
> She is used to this sort of thing.
> Her blacks crackle and drag.

It is a poem of great peace and resignation, utterly without
self-pity. Even with a subject so appallingly close she remains an artist, absorbed in the practical task of letting
each image develop a full, still life of its own. That she is
writing about her own death is almost irrelevant. There is
another poem, "Words," also very late, which is about the
way language remains and echoes long after the turmoil
of life has passed; like "Edge" it has the same translucent
calm. If these were the last things she wrote, I think she

must in the end have accepted the logic of the life she had been leading, and come to terms with its terrible necessities.

Around six A.M. she went up to the children's room and left a plate of bread and butter and two mugs of milk, in case they should wake hungry before the *au pair* girl arrived. Then she went back down to the kitchen, sealed the door and window as best she could with towels, opened the oven, laid her head in it, and turned on the gas.

The Australian girl arrived punctually at nine A.M. She rang and knocked a long time but could get no answer. So she went off to search for a telephone kiosk in order to phone the agency and make sure she had the right address. Sylvia's name, incidentally, was not on either of the doorbells. Had everything been normal, the neighbor below would have been up by then; even if he had overslept, the girl's knocking should have aroused him. But as it happened, the neighbor was very deaf and slept without his hearing aid. More important, his bedroom was immediately below Sylvia's kitchen. The gas seeped down and knocked him out cold. So he slept on through all the noise. The girl returned and tried again, still without success. Again she went off to telephone the agency and ask what to do; they told her to go back. It was now about eleven o'clock. This time she was lucky: some builders had arrived to work in the frozen-up house, and they let her in. When she knocked on Sylvia's door there was no answer and the smell of gas was overpowering. The builders forced the lock and found Sylvia sprawled in the kitchen. She was still warm. She had left a note saying, "Please call Dr.——" and giving his telephone number. But it was too late.

Had everything worked out as it should—had the gas not drugged the man downstairs, preventing him from opening the front door to the *au pair* girl—there is no doubt she would have been saved. I think she wanted to be; why else leave her doctor's telephone number? This time, unlike the occasion ten years before, there was too much holding her to life. Above all, there were the children: she was too passionate a mother to want to lose them or them to lose her. There were also the extraordinary creative powers she now unequivocally knew she possessed: the poems came daily, unbidden and unstoppable, and she was again working on a novel about which, at last, she had no reservations.

WHY, THEN, did she kill herself? In part, I suppose, it was "a cry for help" which fatally misfired. But it was also a last, desperate attempt to exorcise the death she had summoned up in her poems. I have already suggested that perhaps she had begun to write obsessively about death for two reasons. First, when she and her husband separated, however mutual the arrangement, she went through again the same piercing grief and bereavement she had felt as a child when her father, by his death, seemed to abandon her. Second, I believe she thought her car crash the previous summer had set her free; she had paid her dues, qualified as a survivor, and could now write about it. But, as I have written elsewhere, for the artist himself art is not necessarily therapeutic; he is not automatically relieved of his fantasies by expressing them. Instead, by some perverse logic of creation, the act of formal expression may simply make the dredged-up material more readily available to him. The result of handling it in his work may well be that he finds himself living it out. For the artist, in short, nature often imitates art. Or, to restate the cliché, when an artist holds a mirror up to nature he finds out who and what he is; but the knowledge may change him irredeemably so that he becomes that image.

I think Sylvia, in one way or another, sensed this. In an introductory note she wrote to "Daddy" for the BBC, she said of the poem's narrator, "she has to act out the awful little allegory once over before she is free of it." The allegory in question was, as she saw it, the struggle in her between a fantasy Nazi father and a Jewish mother. But perhaps it was also a fantasy of containing in herself her own dead father, like a woman possessed by a demon (in the poem she actually calls him a vampire). In order for her to be free of him, he has to be released like a genie from a bottle. And this is precisely what the poems did: they bodied forth the death within her. But they also did so in an intensely living and creative way. The more she wrote about death, the stronger and more fertile her imaginative world became. And this gave her everything to live for.

I suspect that in the end she wanted to have done with the theme once and for all. But the only way she could find was "to act out the awful little allegory once over." She had always been a bit of a gambler, used to taking risks. The authority of her poetry was in part due to her brave persistence in following the thread of her inspiration right down to the Minotaur's lair. And this psychic courage had its parallel in her physical arrogance and carelessness. Risks didn't frighten her; on the contrary, she found them stimulating. Freud has written, "Life loses in interest, when the highest stake in the game of living, life itself, may not be risked." Finally, Sylvia took that risk. She gambled for the last time, having worked out that the odds were in her favor, but perhaps, in her depression, not much caring whether she won or lost. Her calculations went wrong and she lost.

It was a mistake, then, and out of it a whole myth has grown. I don't think she would have found it much to her taste, since it is a myth of the poet as a sacrificial victim, offering herself up for the sake of her art, having been dragged by the Muses to that final altar through every kind of distress. In these terms, her suicide becomes the whole point of the story, the act which validates her poems, gives them their interest, and proves her seriousness. So people are drawn to her work in much the same spirit as *Time* featured her at length: not for the poetry but for the gossipy, extraliterary "human interest." Yet just as the suicide adds nothing at all to the poetry, so the myth of Sylvia as a passive victim is a total perversion of the woman she was. It misses altogether her liveliness, her intellectual appetite and harsh wit, her great imaginative resourcefulness and vehemence of feeling, her control. Above all, it misses the courage with which she was able to turn disaster into art. The pity is not that there is a myth of Sylvia Plath but that the myth is not simply that of an enormously gifted poet whose death came recklessly, by mistake, and too soon.

I used to think of her brightness as a façade, as though she were able, in a rather schizoid way, to turn her back on her suffering for the sake of appearances, and pretend it didn't exist. But maybe she was also able to keep her unhappiness in check because she could write about it, because she knew she was salvaging from all those horrors something rather marvelous. The end came when she felt she could stand the subject no longer. She had written it out and was ready for something new.

> The blood-jet is poetry,
> There is no stopping it.

The only method of stopping it she could see, her vision by then blinkered by depression and illness, was that last gamble. So having, as she thought, arranged to be saved, she lay down in front of the gas oven almost hopefully, almost with relief, as though she were saying, "Perhaps this will set me free."

ON FRIDAY, February 15th, there was an inquest in the drab, damp coroner's court behind Camden Town: muttered evidence, long silences, the Australian girl in tears. Earlier that morning I had gone with Ted to the undertakers in Mornington Crescent. The coffin was at the far end of a bare, draped room. She lay stiffly, a ludicrous ruff at her neck. Only her face showed. It was gray and slightly transparent, like wax. I had never before seen a dead person and I hardly recognized her; her features seemed too thin and sharp. The room smelled of apples, faint, sweet but somehow unclean, as though the apples were beginning to rot. I was glad to get out into the cold and noise of the dingy streets. It seemed impossible that she was dead.

Even now I find it hard to believe. There was too much life in her long, flat, strongly boned body, and her longish face with its fine brown eyes, shrewd and full of feeling. She was practical and candid, passionate and compassionate. I believe she was a genius. I sometimes catch myself childishly thinking I'll run into her walking on Primrose Hill or the Heath, and we'll pick up the conversation where we left off. But perhaps that is because her poems still speak so distinctly in her accents: quick, sardonic, unpredictable, effortlessly inventive, a bit angry, and always utterly her own.

My Olson Elegy

Irving Feldman

> *I set out now*
> *in a box upon the sea.* Maximus VI

THREE weeks, and now I hear!
What a headstart for the other elegists!
I say, No matter! by any route and manner
we shall arrive beside you together.
Envy, Triumph, Pride, Derision:
such passionate oarsmen drive my harpooneer,
he hurls himself through your side.
You lie and wait to be overtaken.
You absent yourself at every touch.

It was an adolescent, a poetboy,
who told me—one of that species, spoiled,
self-showing, noisy, conceited, *épatants,*—
voice breaking from the ego-distance like
a telephone's, not a voice indeed
but one in facsimile, recon-
stituted static, a locust voice,
exhumed, resurrected, chirring
in its seventeenth year, contentedly
saying, "And I've just completed
section fifteen of my Olson elegy."

Landscape on legs, old Niagara!—all
the unique force, the common vacancy,
the silence and seaward tumultuous gorge
slowly clogging with your own *disjecta,*
tourists, trivia, history,
disciples, picnickers in hell;
oh great Derivative in quest!
of your own unknown author, the source

—flying bit of the beginning blast,
a sky-shard where early thunder slumbers,
the first syllabic grunt, a danger,
a nameless name, a tap on the head; you,
Olson!, whale, thrasher, bard of bigthink,
your cargo of ambergris and pain,
your steamy stupendous sputtering
—all apocalypse and no end:
precocious larvae have begun to try
the collected works beneath your battered sides.

See them now! dazzling elegists sitting
on their silvery kites on air
like symbols in flight, swooping daredevils
jockey for position, mount a hasty breeze
and come careening at your vastness
to tread among the gulls and plover
—but the natural cries of birds do not
console us for our gift of speech.
Embarrassed before the sea and silence,
we do not rise or sing,
wherefore this choir of eternal boys
strut and sigh and puff their chests and stare
outward from the foundering beach.

King of the flowering deathboat, falls,
island, leviathan, starship night,
you plunge to the primitive deep
where satire's puny dreadful monsters,
its Follies and its Vices, cannot reach,
and swim among their lost originals
—free, forgotten, powerful, moving
wholly in a universe of rhythm—
and re-enter your own first Fool,
inventing happiness out of nothing.
You are the legend death and the sea have seized
in order to become explicable.

—Smell of salt is everywhere,
speed and space burn monstrousness
away, exaltation blooms in the clear:
fair weather, great *bonanza*, the high,
swelling treasure, blue catch of heaven!
The swimmer like the sea reaches every shore.
Superlative song levitates from lips

of the glowing memorialists,
their selves flash upward in the sun.

Now you are heavier than earth, everything
has become lighter than the air.

The Titanic

Irving Feldman

SECRET in a woman's coat, her hat,
his face hidden by a veil, crazy
with fear and shame there among women
and children shivering in the boat,
he escaped huddled over an oar
on the cold and coldly misted sea.
His last sight was the deck awash and screaming.
Sick to the depths of his stomach,
he retched on the gray Newfoundland shore
and drowned in the bitter syncope.
Under a hovel roof, he woke
naked in a woman's arms and could
remember nothing, having become
what henceforth he would call *himself*.

One hundred fathoms down, withdrawn
from every future and larger than life,
with nothing left to lose or wish, the Titans
sit in their eternal afterglow
and with glorious instruments—
curving, belled, and fluted, the fruits
of a golden age—blow upward,
in vast unison and bubbling serenity,
toward the solemn void, the dizzying precipice,
God Save the King!

To Byzantium

Andrew Fetler

A MONG MY brother's effects in the cardboard box I
brought home from the state hospital at Newhall, California, was a photo of my mother—her last formal portrait
at 71—and, stuck in the frame, a snapshot of himself. The
snapshot shows him standing on the steps of our church
in the Los Feliz hills overlooking Los Angeles. Feet apart,
arms folded over his chest, head high in half profile. So
he had treasured this snapshot. I had taken it eight years
ago, the day after we buried our father. My brother had
marked an X in the gravel before the church, the spot
where I was to stand with his camera, and I had watched
him through the viewfinder as he struck his pose and gave
me the word to snap the picture.

He loved being photographed, to record important moments in his life. I had taken pictures of him in the
cemetery, where he had stood meditating at our father's
grave. And next morning he got the flash attachment and
had me photograph him sitting at our father's desk, pen in
hand and an expression of deep thought on his face. After
lunch he dragged me out again, and there we were, before
our father's church.

"That's wrong," he said, before I could snap the picture.
"I should be facing the door." He faced the church door
and struck his pose again, head high and arms folded.
"How's this?"

"Great."

"Are you getting the cross on the door?"

I hadn't noticed. "I'm getting it," I said. "Are you ready?"

He drew a deep breath and pushed out his chest. "Go
ahead."

The doctor at Newhall said my brother had swallowed enough pills to kill a horse.

He never showed me this picture, and now that I have it I feel mildly surprised at seeing the resemblance between my father and my brother. In life, the only resemblance I saw was that between the real thing and a distorted copy. In my mind I had never admitted my brother to my father's company.

But I had not known my father when he was as young as my brother. In my earliest family album is a yellowed snapshot of my father on those same church steps in 1921, when he broke with his American patriarch. Except for his beard and priestly robes, he looks like my brother's double—feet pugnaciously apart, the points of his shoes sticking out from under the hem of his cassock, head high in half profile, and arms folded inappropriately over the cross on his chest, as if he had forgotten this burden hanging by a chain from his neck. The same stance of defiance as my brother's, the same self-conscious air of nobility and Old World earnestness and innocence of irony. Father and son.

My father was one of those rare émigrés who came out intact one step ahead of the Revolution. With nobody but God to guide him, he sank his entire inheritance into the church and the hillside it stood on, which he christened Old Russia, only to see his inspiration frowned upon by his new ecclesiastical superiors, whom he had thought to surprise and delight with his monument to Holy Russia.

What the difficulty was, exactly, I don't know. Unlike my brother, I could never appreciate theological niceties. I suspect that my father's quarrel with his superiors in 1921 was less a matter of theology than taste. These beardless American priests with their cars and radios could be expected to look doubtfully at a church that seemed made of Christmas cookies and peppermint sticks, and wonder at its builder. His eventual excommunication, which he lived to regret, made him no less Orthodox in his own eyes. He revived liturgical variants heard since the seventeenth century only in the Monastery of the Grottoes in Kiev. He dedicated an arbor in our garden to the memory of an ancient abbot, and hung an image of St. Vladimir in the church beside the Holy Mother of Kazan.

I have a funny friend in Boston, an Irishman, who bangs the table with his fist when he talks, and having yelled himself out asks with a timid smile, "Isn't it?" or, "Am I not right?" He likes to hear about Old Russia. His father was a boozing Irish Catholic, a Boston patriot who bounced through the streets on a fat beer horse, at the head of his precinct on the Fourth. And although his father's memory embarrasses him, he will arise and go to Galway and Galway Bay, and parade through town with hat and cane and two fine setters in leash, some day. Yet his irreligion is loud and emphatic. When he talks about religion he seems to be talking about sexual repression, and his voice loses the resonance I hear in his Irish jokes.

His example cautions me. As a child I must have been exposed to a good deal of resonance. I had an edifying hallucination, for example. I saw the great Los Angeles fire when I was six, which engulfed the houses and temples and plazas from Hollywood to Santa Monica. I stood by the gates of our Old Russia in the Los Feliz hills, between the Swiss chalet and the Taj on adjoining hills, and watched the smoke roiling over the rooftops far below. The merchandise of gold and silver, and precious stones, and of pearls, and fine linen, and purple, and silk, and scarlet, and all thyine wood, and all manner vessels of ivory, and all manner vessels of most precious wood, and of brass, and iron, and marble, and cinnamon, and odors, and ointments, and wine, and oil, and fine flour, and wheat, and beasts, and sheep, and horses, and bodies, and souls of men—all up in smoke in that city, wherein were made rich all that had ships in the sea by reason of her costliness. My father's incantations at the table lulled me to sleep in those days. I may have seen a movie of a city burning. I asked my brother, my senior by seven years, and of course Los Angeles had enjoyed no such conflagration. But I know the revulsion Los Angeles arouses in travelers. One fine morning those miles of glitter will be gone and the desert stretch to the horizon where the city had stood.

Our own forty acres of poplars and silver birches, like the Taj on the next hill, were rented to film companies.

Nothing was native to the place—neither plants nor people, nor religion. My father built Old Russia because he could not go back to his century. We did not read Soviet writers there, but the old romantics. You left your car by the wooden gates and walked up an avenue of poplars to the priest's house. I must have been thirteen or fourteen when I realized that we had become professional ethnics. You might see my parents slouching in rattan chairs on the veranda, the samovar steaming between them. My brother would be playing old liturgical music on the upright in the parlor within, cluttering the music with expansive ornaments all his own, trills and gorgeous arabesques, giving expression to his sense of well-being and delusions.

There would be a reason for my brother's musical inventions. He was tormented by the imperatives of moral purity in the morning, crushing boredom and drowsiness at noon, and lust at night. He had a passion for logic and could spot inconsistencies, and picked fights, interrogated, quarreled. I don't know if he ever changed anybody's mind, but he claimed victories in the meeting halls he frequented in his exhausting search for God and women, among the sects and societies that litter California's coast. He could not sin deliberately, with a will, but only on the sly, behind his own back. Then he confessed his sins to his own heart, damned himself, and read poetry about the night of the soul. In this manner he purified himself, and at the piano added grace notes in transports of redeemed innocence.

I sat on the couch doing my homework. He played the piano with his head thrown back and eyes closed. Communing. A strong scent of lilac drifted in through the open window. Then the vacuum cleaner began to whine upstairs, and the music stopped. Above the noise of the vacuum cleaner we could hear our mother singing to herself.

"What is she doing?" he said, glaring at the ceiling.

"She's vacuuming your bedroom."

He turned on the piano stool. Whenever he bothered to look at me I had to brace myself for some challenge or other. "Why," he said, folding his arms, "are you sitting there? I'm really interested."

"I'm doing my homework," I said piously.

"What homework?"

"Math, if you must know."

"What will you do with math? What will you measure? This house? I mean, how is it with people like you? Do you ever stop to think *why* you do anything? Or do you just do your homework, as you say?"

"I don't know," I said, to irritate him, and gave him my stupid look.

"Fascinating. You eat, you sleep, you run about like a dog. Doesn't it hurt you to live like a dog?"

At that moment our mother appeared on the stairs with a red kerchief on her head and a rag in her hand. "Did you throw a razor blade in the sink?" she asked him.

"That's all right," he said. "I have more."

My father, too, found it painful to live with one foot on earth. Nothing consoled him for his expulsion from Russia, and in the wild hills above Los Angeles he fought off barbaric America to preserve a quality, a tone, a style. In his defiant days he had built Old Russia to the glory of God with materials scarcely more convincing than those of Disneyland. Old Russia transported him to Byzantium. He could not turn from that dream, and sought to restore his losses with plaster and paint.

Our wooden church walls were made to look like stone three feet thick, but they housed a real church. My father was an actor, yet a priest. The rituals were charades, yet redemptive. Everything was faked except the corpses in our cemetery behind the church. The corpses were real. The years had decimated Old Russia. The resourceful in my father's congregation, the born criminals, caught on to insurance in Toledo, Ohio, or the stock market in Chicago. The old were dumped by their children in commercial nursing homes. A nervous poet who used to walk our paths with a book under his arm tried Mexico and cut his wrists. "In this life to die is nothing new—but to live, of course, is not new, either." And the second-generation children roared up the hill in blue and red sports cars of a Sunday morning, to see the religious antics their folks had been up to a million years ago. When they slammed out to the beaches, the dust they kicked up drifted in the sun past the veranda with its rattan chairs and samovar stand.

Two old babas lived forever, it seemed. Long black

skirts, white kerchiefs, chattering up the path, taking Easter cakes to the church. Inside, they kissed the stone floor which I was supposed to have mopped. Down on all fours like two wolves, pressing their mouths to the stone, drinking the spirit. They kissed holy pictures, walls under pictures, each other, and my father's hand when he approached in his priestly robes. He suffered them, and loved them, but sought refuge at the altar, turning his back on the thirty unbelievers who had been herded in from the heat outside from a sightseeing bus parked by the gates.

Small-town librarians and schoolteachers, in respectful attitudes, hands folded, their faces stiff and reserved, noses sniffing the incense in the artificial darkness, eyes staring at the flame before the Holy Mother, and feet edging toward a wall or pillar as the service dragged on. He refused to install chairs or even benches, as in the valley the Greek Orthodox had done, and would not cut a minute of his interminable ritual. Two sightseeing companies in Hollywood struck him from their itineraries, and Pleasure Tours complained they were stopping too long between the Taj and Homes Of The Stars. But the priest worked the altar as if God's clemency depended upon it. The church choir had long since disappeared, to be replaced by my brother at the organ in the balcony, where he played his responses to my father's exclamations at the altar, yanked the rope that rang the bell, and squinted down at girls like a prisoner from his cage.

We rotted on that hillside as if cut off from the Body of Christ, not serving but catering, tourists having replaced believers. From time to time, when threatened by bankruptcy, we sold bits and pieces of Old Russia to subdividers. Pretentious houses crawled up the hillside, with billboards advertising "Paradise Now!" and "Heavenly View!" The sick old man, cornered by Los Angeles, clutched his stomach with one hand and dragged himself up and down our paths, around the church, to the cemetery and back, lashed by the far din of the construction gangs.

No continuing city. He grew small and bent, and forgot to comb his beard, but remembered to greet my mother in the kitchen, on the morning of Easter Sunday: "Christ is risen!" And she answered, "Verily, He is risen!" He delayed going to church as long as possible, cooling his tea in the saucer and playing with a vest-button hanging by a thread. I sat watching him. A boy of fifteen can hurt to see his priest and emperor reduced to a caterer.

"Dad?" I said. "Why do the tourists have to come on Easter Sunday?"

"Don't bother him now," my mother said. "Go find your brother. It's time we started for church."

"I can't tell them to go away," my father said to her.

"Of course not."

"Jesus died for them, too. What would He think of me?" And he gave me an astonished look.

From the gates the Pleasure Tours bus honked twice to announce its arrival, on Easter Sunday as on any morning, starting him to his feet. Then my brother, twenty-two at the time, whom I once caught in the vestry trying on our father's priestly robes, stuck his head in at the door and yelled, "We're late!"—and ran.

My father hobbled out the back way. I followed him the length of our garden and out over a turnstile beyond the church grounds proper, the long way around, past construction lumber and foundation pits gouged in the hillside, over land no longer ours, to avoid visitors with cameras. In the old days he used to like being photographed. No more. Now, he stole into the vestry by the back door, and we did not speak as I attended him and he dressed for the show that was not a show. He took the amethyst from the jewel box I held for him, and put it on his finger. He took the chain and kissed the cross and hung it round his neck. When he was ready, when it was time to show himself to the people, he turned instead to the mirror beside the alcove.

I saw an expression of curiosity flickering in his eyes. In the balcony my brother had started the music for his cue, but here the priest stood, absorbed by his image in the dark glass, seeming not to know himself, forgetting his vocation. Then he caught my eye in the mirror. "After all is said and done—" he began, but did not finish. We stood looking at each other, father and son, and when his cue came and went and he did not move, I knew something awful was happening.

Priest, father, emperor in his splendid robes, he stood looking at me with a petrified expression in his eyes. His lip gave a twitch, and all at once he sank to one knee and embraced me. Pulled me into his arms and held. My confusion cut loose from my lungs a short, choppy, derisive laugh, like a bark, and he leaned away, his body wobbling on one knee as if I had plunged a dagger into his chest. He screwed up one eye, giving me an uncomprehending look.

"Tell them to go away, Dad. Please? Tell them to go *away!*"

Then he understood, and he wrung my name from his throat as if I had been weeping all along, all along. I fled. I ran the length of Old Russia in the fragrant morning, and hiding in a pile of lumber heard the bell strike, and burst into tears.

We never drew so close again. At fifteen I did not know how, and he denied himself his last vanity—a son's love.

About that time my brother discovered his mission: to stop the religious freak show in Old Russia and turn the church to a true worship of the Divine Spirit. My brother felt more comfortable with the Divine Spirit than with God and Jesus Christ. But he could not speak of such reforms to our father, and bided his time running after girls in the I-Thou Temple in Hollywood.

He sat on the veranda after dinner, reading the paper and burping. He had always been too old to play with me, absorbed in matters too elevated for my understanding, but he liked to instruct. If I wanted to sit with him, I had to be instructed.

"Where's Dad?" he said, as I sat down beside him.

"In his room."

My brother put down the paper. "He doesn't know what he's talking about. He's never been to the I-Thou Temple. It's not at all like the Church of the Open Door. At the I-Thou it's all interpersonal. Do you know what that means?"

"No."

"That means your fellow man is not an It, he's a Thou. If you treat a person as a thing—as Dad treats me, for example—you only isolate yourself. We call it alienation.

That's what Dad suffers from—alienation. He's finished."

It would have seemed so, at first glance. From my brother too the old man averted his face. He subsided and sank from us, deaf to us, locked up in himself. One thing remained for him to do, to unburden himself of a last burden, without debate, without seeking my mother's counsel. Clutching his stomach, he had my brother drive him down the hill to the District Court to have his name changed from Viliki to Krotki. To the judge who granted his prayer neither name meant anything. Viliki means great, and Krotki means gentle.

I could not make a fuss about the new name devolving upon me as a minor. With a different breakfast in his stomach, my father might have chosen a name like Unknown, or Clean Spit. But my brother stormed, wanting his father's true name. And he kept his father's true name, having attained his majority when our father humbled himself.

I went away to college, and to war. And when I came home from the war, when I myself felt like a tourist in Old Russia, I saw my father sitting in his rattan chair on the veranda. He blinked his watery eyes at me and pulled from his pocket a caramel coated with dust and a curling white hair. "For your sweet tooth." He had the quiet insanity of a well-behaved child. He made a joke about his new name which he repeated at odd moments at the table, diverting him more than us. "Yes, it's true," he would say, apropos of nothing. "I went out great, and the Lord has brought me home again gentle."

In my mind I have a heaven for him, and a chair to sit in, by reason of that same disastrous Sunday morning, when after all was said and done he wished to abide if he could in Jesus Christ, that he might have confidence and not be ashamed before Him at His coming.

So he died. And my brother felt born again. He played with his father's jewels, wore his father's tattered bathrobe, slammed doors, and ignored the dinner bell as his father had ignored it before him.

Having heard the icy call of the Lord, my brother assumed that he was chosen. He believed every spirit that came to plead with him from every corner of his possessed soul. My brother the inheritor stretched his arms as if waking from a long sleep, yawned, smiled, spat. Alive to himself, not doubting himself, not puzzling himself. And went out to look at Old Russia, to see what all needed to be done, and had me photograph him on the church steps for an historical record, his feet apart and arms folded over his chest, not having been shot dead to himself by the Implacable Hunter.

He still ran after girls at the I-Thou Temple in Hollywood, and came home to argue that nothing could revive Old Russia except an ecumenical spirit. He spent an afternoon framing a photo of our mother for his nightstand. "We have a date Saturday, you and I," he joked with her.

No joke. He took her out to rich dinners she could not eat and movies that put her to sleep. He brought her home exhausted and confused, and at midnight shook her from her snooze in her rocker, and dragged her to his bedroom for prayers, to pray with him as she had prayed with our father. "Yes, yes," she would say, staring about at the charts and religious posters and mystical symbols on his walls. "Yes, dearest, let us pray. God will forgive everything." He kept her on her knees for thirty minutes, as he read from some greasy pamphlet or other, and sent her to bed with a reminder that they had a date Saturday. Then he sulked for days and ignored her, and prayed and fasted alone by her photo in his bedroom.

In our climate every conceivable religious plant creeps, slithers, entwines, snaps, exhales, twists, breeds in the sun. My brother felt at home in this jungle. He knew what to do and how to go about it. Not to repeat his father's mistakes, he did not have himself ordained, but took care to be licensed by the I-Thou Temple. He sat at his father's desk, stuffing his head with catalogues of metaphysical distinctions and occult fads. Late at night he pored over geometric figures, circles detached and overlapping, and triangles with an eye at the apex, and crosses formed by the asymptotes of hyperbolas, and psychospiritual organizational tables that would have impressed General Motors, and calendars of duties, and charts tracing his personal oscillations through the darkness and the light. During my visits, I might have learned something about him if he had expressed a preference for chocolate ice cream over vanilla. But he had become a Deep Thinker and was not accessible.

When next I visited, a small billboard had been erected over the gates. "Welcome To The I-Thou Russian Church." The parent Temple in Hollywood encouraged him to keep what he liked of the old rituals and wardrobe. For two years our scandalized Orthodox remnants probed the thickets of a lawsuit against my brother, and settled out of court for the best slice of the land, where they proposed building a modern Orthodox church with indirect lighting. Old Russia was reduced to the priest's house, the church, and the cemetery.

"How I pray he marries!" my mother said to me in the kitchen, cutting away the rot from potatoes. She had grown old and had begun to forget English and sometimes sprinkled sugar on her stew. "You must know some good girls. Can't you take him away from here, to meet your friends?"

"My friends are trivial. He's too deep for them."

"Why are you nasty? You know nothing about him."

"Don't you care what he did to the church?" I asked.

"Did what! Now we have a fire insurance! If it burns down we can build again."

My brother never found the wife he thought he wanted, the young girl his fancy installed at the organ in the church balcony while he celebrated the I-Thou mysteries at the altar. The balcony spot went to a paid organist from a Fundamentalist radio station that advertised professional anti-Communists, itinerant faith-healers, and blest handkerchiefs. With the help of this musicologist he put together a service from the more dramatic parts of the Orthodox ritual and Fundamentalist clatter. The tourist clientele fell off, the Orthodox ceased altogether, but varieties of existentialists got wind of the new thing in Old Russia and flocked up the hill.

His success should not have astonished me, I realize now. He was a compulsive talker, loved to preach, and during a Latin collect he moved our father's Bible from the gospel side of the altar to the epistle side without rhyme or reason. In the vestry after the service he asked me to help him

with his robes. "How was I?" I had never seen him so
elated. He offered me the job of sacristan—room, board,
and pocket money. Well, how was he? When you stripped
his sermon of fashionable words like *existential* and *ambi-
ence,* and mystical pretensions, and a love of spectacle,
you saw a simple commitment to the old verities. Seeing
him there in our father's priestly robes, pulling in the new
breed of celebrants who lounged about in comfortable
Balaban & Katz chairs—"No Smoking!"—I thought the
church felt as secure from disintegration as it had felt in
the old days, before Pleasure Tours and subdividers had
sniffed its carcass.

Tea on the veranda as in the old days, and the lilac
bloomed. My brother ran into the house to fetch his Plato,
and came out turning the pages of the book nearsightedly,
impatient to enlighten my dark mind with Plato's delightful
passage about the heavenly pattern. He coupled his rhetorical questions with other questions and other premises,
breeding monsters of logic with several heads and tails,
but I understood him to mean that we lived in a finite
universe, and the earth stood fixed at the center of the
spheres of sun and moon, the stars and all the planets. He
did not say these antiquated things, but with the lilac's
thick fragrance in the air he made me feel them, and I
thought him beautiful as he read, holding the book close
to his nose: "'In heaven,' I replied, 'there is laid up a
pattern of it, methinks, which he who desires may behold,
and beholding, may set his own house in order. But whether
such a one exists, or ever will exist in fact, is no matter;
for he will live after the manner of that city, having nothing
to do with any other.'"

"That's good," I said.

"How can you say that's good," my brother cried, "and
not believe? If you don't believe, then you are not moved.
If you are moved, then you must believe."

"All right, I believe."

"But you don't! Why are you lying?"

IN THOSE last days, before my mother's death and my
brother's commitment to the state hospital at Newhall, if
you happened to come by on a quiet afternoon, left your

car by the white gates and walked up the avenue of poplars
to the priest's house, you might have seen the old woman
sweeping the veranda, and heard the piano tinkling in the
dark house within. She would have been anxious to please
you, and might have taken it into her head to show you
the church. Descending sideways down the steps, favoring
her stiff leg, she would have approached you with her
hands clasped in an expression of pleasure. A new face!

What part of Russia did you come from? Had you known
her husband? *This way, this way!* she would gesture, her
English fading. She might tug at your sleeve and step back
to have a better look at you, working her gums, smiling and
pointing to the church. Did you come to see the church?
You would look into the trees where she pointed and see
something golden and white behind the green foliage. *So
nice, so nice!* she would seem to say, laughing soundlessly,
and start up the path. *That's right, come along, I'll show
you everything!* You would follow past neglected flower-
beds and unpruned bushes, past a dilapidated arbor and a
rain-warped orange crate standing in the high grass and
nettles. At a turn in the path by a dead lemon tree she
would suddenly stop and stretch her neck forward like a
buzzard, to see if the church was still there. Yes, her old
eyes could see it still, and she would give you a look of
infinite gaiety. Could you see it? Could you see what she
saw?

You might, if you happened to be in Plato's mood.

If not, you would see that the church in Old Russia was
not a bad tourist stop, as such attractions go, the blue doors
and windows decorated like Christmas cookies, the pillars
twisted into candy sticks, and the large golden onion at
the top sprinkled with blue stars. This dome, you would
see, pleased the artist enough to add two small domes
as an afterthought, asymmetrically, one near the main door
and the other half sunk behind the vestry gable. Something
to photograph, if you photograph such things.

But if you did not calculate the uses of such a place and
were in no hurry to see the Taj, if for once you were
neither rich nor poor, felt neither trapped nor abandoned
by life, and sensed a momentary order in your soul, you
might have stopped beside the old woman and stood still

with a small intake of breath, and heard the wind in the grass and seen the church floating in the sky.

The old woman who had blossomed there, and was soon to die like her lemon tree, would not trouble her mad son for the keys. Giving the church door a shake to show that it was really locked, she would pull you round to a smaller path grown over with weeds, where the thick bushes darkened the earth and the damp air would chill your feet.

This way, this way!—and you would follow her to the very spot where Emil Richter filmed the closing scene for his *Fathers and Sons*. The willow he planted grows aslant the stagnant pond to this day, hanging its unkempt head over rockweed, skunk cabbage, pond scums, stoneworts. As you approached you might hear the plash of a toad, and lifting your eyes see the luminous algae glowing darkly with emanations from the dead. Mr. Richter was fond of a melancholy little bench, where Bazarov's old father sat watching as his wife touched up their son's grave. For years that bench lay overturned in the grass behind the compost heap, but when my father died my mother dragged the bench to his grave.

"My husband," she would tell you, smiling gaily and inviting you to sit and look at death. "Did you know him?"

The Vampire

John DeWitt

When I entertained Ruskin
there were still things to talk about.
We talked about religious art.
I never lusted for him.

The peasants eat garlic.
Their breaths are foul.
I cannot bear their company.

I enjoy a poem by Robert Browning
just before dawn. He is good company.

The boring thing about the peasants
is that they never notice the obvious.
They are easily fooled at night.

I have had all the young bodies
that I desired. I continue
to pursue them to keep amused.
At times though, I long
for a glimpse of the sun.
I am not different from my lovers.

The townspeople are so stupid that one is forced
to be cruel with them, or at least to make
jokes at their expense. They offer no
resistance. They are so vulnerable,

like little animals. Sooner or later
a young boy will swing his cat by the tail.

The most interesting aspect
of seduction
is at the moment they offer me
their loins
and I take their throats.

There is a certain pattern to each night:
the tour of the castle, the walk
in the garden, the search in my own way
for new appetites.

I have never dreamt while I slept,
although recently I have been disturbed
by the feeling when I awake that I have
been somewhere, that I have been someone else.
I can almost feel warmth. It is most upsetting.

As for living, ha, ha, there are the servants.

The first thing I ask a new one, before
he or she will spend a night here,
is to choose between a Rodin and a Boccioni.
Then I know. I cannot afford to waste time.

A long time ago when I had the energy
I would walk through the village
in the fog and amuse myself
with a lusty wench or young farmboy.
I also enjoyed playing the bat
while old women prayed their way to sleep.

I am tired. The new ones are lazy.
Rather than go out
I find them stupidly sucking on sheep,

dogs, anything that wanders by.
They have no taste.

There is no other place to go.
I was on the Mediterranean last season
where there were plenty of interesting
young bodies but they were all so dull
that I could not bear them. The motorcar is vulgar.

The castle is run down.
My paintings are covered with dust.
My new companions lust over television.
They enjoy the gray figures
moving before them.

I especially enjoy being alone
at the instant before dawn, when the transformation
is about to take place. Everything is so still
and then I must rush back. It is very exciting.

Walter Pater warned me what would happen.

The last interview I had was a terrible
disappointment. Not only was I misquoted
but the interviewer was a boring little snipe.
There was also some trouble with the camera.

Introduction to Dome-Building:
A Geodesic Meditation

Michael Rossman

1. I WRITE this in the nursery I have just built for the ferns and our son Lorca. Opening out from a hole in a wall of our cottage, it is a modified geodesic structure spanning an irregular space. Entirely skinned in transparent and tinted plastics, and sheltered by a small bamboo grove, it defines a magical space, an experience of outside inside. Its snug twin insulating skins scarcely interrupt the continuity of green life, from bamboo to planter over the bed. The two ⅜-caps forming its airy roof are as light as they look, maybe fifty pounds, and already have held in a gale wind. Their patterns of triangle/pentagon/hexagon, tinted in the yellow/green/blue chord of bamboo against open sky, form the two wings of the butterfly of Mathematics. Lights and gems will be his hovering eyes, to complete the image for the child in his crib, and for us as we lie on the floor in meditation. Poor and cramped for space even without a child, we needed it. And joyful energy rises up in me, the payoff from elegance in response to necessity.

Total cost: maybe $150, a week's learning, two weeks' work.

2. I FIRST turned on to geodesics by reading Bucky Fuller. But what kindled my longing to do was the poetry of Steve Baer's *Dome Cookbook*,[1] which describes the related but distinct technology of *zomes* which he helped develop. Beginning with the work of modern Russian crys-

[1] Lama Foundation, Box 422, Corrales, New Mexico 87048. $1.00.

tallographers and mathematicians, Baer extends their results in theory, translates this into architectural design, and
describes the process of constructing *zomes* out of recycled
sheet metal from the tops of junked cars—and how not to
chop your foot off if you salvage them with an ax. Spectral
clusters of *zomes* now stand as funky monuments of collective creation at Lama, high in the sparse mountains of New
Mexico. And *Dome Cookbook* circulates in the countercul-
ture, bearing its implicit testament of a man who salvaged
the skills of his technological training and put them to the
uses of the imagination.

Closer to home, at Pacific School, an experimental high
school down south of S.F. Bay, ten domes were built in
four months, three by the students alone. In *Domebook I* [2]
the builders tell how—a full practical introduction to theory,
different material technologies, design and construction
problems, aesthetics, etc., put together in two weeks. It
gave me all I needed for the nursery, besides its own delight.

3. IT IS THE BREATH of new example, imagination come
alive, which inspires us to new behavior. I could sit around
reading Bucky Fuller till Domesday. But to see before me,
in their own handwriting and funky home photos, ex-
mathematicians and freed 15-year-olds casually multiplying
spherical grace—well, that was something else.

Both domebooks were put together, printed, and distributed by a cluster of technologies which place the producing
of a book within easy reach of a semi-skilled, low-capital
work group. This format was first made widely visible
through the *Whole Earth Catalogue*, whose explosive pop-
ularity indicated the audience and felt need for educational
access to technology. Its motto: "We *are* as gods, and
might as well get good at it."

[2] Now *Domebook II*. Pacific Domes, Box 1629, Los Gatos,
California 95030; $3.00. I should also mention the *Inflatocook-
book* for pneumatic nomad domes. Ant Farm, 247 Gate 5 Road,
Sausalito, California; $3.00.

THE TRANSFORMATION
OF PERSONAL CONSCIOUSNESS

4. OUR ARCHITECTURE develops the cube monotonously—though it is only one of the Perfect Forms known to the Pythagoreans and Plato. For them mathematics and theology were configured together. They would not have found strange the notion that living within space generated by other geometrical Forms induces changed consciousness —which is what the current testimony of people who use icosahedron-based geodesics as a technology not only of housing, but of psychological and spiritual centering, boils down to.

5. LIKE OUR SOCIETY, conventional building technology is organized around the concentration of stresses and forces, and their treatment by means of brute local strength and gross load-members. Geodesic technology, like a number of other alternates now spreading, differs not only in its mathematical base, but in its essential dependence upon the structural principle of synergy. Its treatment of force is global and flexible, rather than local and rigid. The linear sum of the strengths of its minimal individual components is multiplied many times into the strength and stability of the whole system, which only appears as the dome is brought to completion as a living structure.

Having built normal houses, I can swear that to build by such principles is a radically unfamiliar experience, and changes your consciousness. Even your routine awareness and trivial mistakes are of a new nature—of combination, permutation, and edge-effect. And I can't describe how at completion you're aware of a new form quickening under your hands, coming alive in a way unknown from usual building. But all dome-builders speak of this moment with awe, and treat their domes as if they were creatures who could be kept in health or wounded.

6. COGNITION BEGINS in the body's action. Under the bones of a forming dome, as the sun marked him with the silhouette of a new spirit, our infant son began to invent geometry. He discovered his fist, and then tried to bring it to his mouth. On the third day of hitting himself in the

eye with the part his vision guided, he recognized that he was not an indivisible point, but parts arranged in spatial relation—and solved the problem by looking off into space and guiding his fist by touch.

Building a dome is a yoga, a stretch of action-road along which consciousness changes. The road's stations are the repeated failures of expectation, and the incremental learning from each. No mystery: the lessons are quite specific. Time and again you design a member or place a prop from a long-accumulating gut sense of what strength is necessary for support; or cramp your body to lean gingerly on a hub. Each time, your expectations prove to be gross or unnecessary, your anticipations are revealed as fearful. And what guides you shifts, from a grasping for security toward a sense of the delicate power of wholeness.

7. FROM OUR experience in the physical world we derive the metaphors which undergird our understanding of all else. We were raised in a Way which taught us that hierarchies of importance, strong and weak members, were implicit in building. What would be the spontaneous politics and social constructions of children who played with struts instead of blocks, and who early internalized a Way of building in which all components were equally essential and effort evenly distributed, and the power of each dependent on and multiplied by cooperation? Is the social image of a geodesic dome a society without strongmen?

SOCIAL DIMENSIONS
OF DOME TECHNOLOGY

8. DOWN TO America, where the Government reports that housing costs average 20–25 percent of a family's reward for production. A family with kids needs roughly 1,000 square feet of floorspace. Conventional building technology costs *begin* at $17–20 per square foot, labor included. The current estimate is that 40 percent of American families cannot afford to own the cheapest new capitalist home. Under our exchange system, such a home costs roughly 2½ years of an average family's productive work. Financing in a profit economy runs this to 4½–5 years. (Taxes and upkeep figure extra.) Cheap prefab construc-

tion can bring these figures down to around $12 per square foot and 3 years' work.

Geodesic buildings equally adequate to physical needs, safe and aesthetic, cost less than $3 per square foot-equivalent for foundation, structure, lofting, and utilities core. This is the cost of materials. They are minimal, and the routines of building are few, simple, and precise. Most are easily hand-automated. So labor is greatly reduced. And its nature is changed. A variety of specialists and their skills are needed for a tract home, but anyone defthanded can build a dome. Thus, even given our present habits with space, an average family can own a dome home for ⅝ year of productive exchange for materials, plus ⅝ man-year of its own labor in building.

9. FROM ANY HUMANE perspective of ecology or economics, our conventional building technologies are enormously wasteful of materials and human work. Low-skill synergic construction technology makes radically more possible the vision of universal adequate housing in America. *Fact,* while our cities choke and rot: one year of the military budget could buy materials and land to house 40,000,000 people well in geodesics—and also to train and pay the men in military servitude to build them within this period.

10. SUCH TECHNOLOGY has political dimensions. It invites user design as well as construction, in each way severing dependence upon specialists and weakening involvement and support of the system built about them, the megamachine of the housing industry. Slashed capitalization requirements weaken user control by the economic system. Aesthetically, technically, financially, the living-unit thus tends to self-determination. Geodesics are a clear example of a technology which empowers people to determine the conditions of their lives.

Any technology points such specific directions; who knows how deeply they already run in us?

(I just flashed on where I first turned on to the possibilities of transparent plastics as a housing material. It was sometime after WW II, I was maybe seven. Donald Duck Comics came out with its first touch of science-fiction, an issue devoted to the future and inspired by the imaginations of GE designers. Donald and his nephews wandered in a world of consumer wonder. Caught in a rainstorm, their host unfolded an infinitesimal square of clear plastic into a tent-umbrella. And I thought, wow, would I like to make a fort out of something like that . . .)

Assembled on modular principles and thus relatively reusable and portable, and permitting a greatly-lessened proportional investment of work in housing, geodesics encourage our drift from being fixed in location to a semi-nomadic life-style more matched to a culture of changes.

11. WHAT DO ALL these abstractions come to, in this time of history? I am a young man with lover and child and friends now facing the choices that will determine our adult lives, and through them the reconstruction of our society. Low cost/skill synergic housing technology grants us radical mobility. After building the nursery, Karen and I know that we can move anywhere, anytime, and make ourselves a home adequate in space and grace for $2,000 worth of materials and a season's labor; and that a group can move together on such terms, and build easily in a way which blends with whatever land receives us. Before this, the straight choice was to be tied to twenty years of payments at a rate which forced you to work at a steady "job," with all that implies. The only option was to build by yourself conventionally, by fragments, while working and renting. Those I know who tried this found the process occupying all of their life's "spare" time for three to five years, and faced any further move reluctantly. So these new technologies free our life-decisions from some heavy constraints.

12. BUT OF COURSE, it's not quite so simple and rosy. Weepy fingers of bamboo hide our nursery dome from the roving search of the city building inspectors, cruising with the fleet of Berkeley police. For to live in a dome is to live beyond the Law—literally, since they are legal only out in country not subject to the Uniform Building Codes.

As with Simon Rodias' towers in Watts, the codes and inspectors comprehend neither the driving impulse nor the structural principles that flower into geodesic domes. Designed to guard human life, the codes base their expectations on cubic architecture and stud-and-beam construction, and arbitrarily outlaw the accomplishments of a more efficient technology—and the social consequences of its wide adoption.

13. IT'S NOT SIMPLY a matter of being behind the times. The Law is not free to change. Great economic and political interests are vested in keeping the codes as they are. For lumber companies, the codes protect and enforce the profitable waste of the planet's dwindling forests. For the closed racist plumbers' and electricians' unions, with their $10 per hour wage scales, the codes outlaw use of the high-efficiency, light, flexible plastic piping and conduit which now make plumbing and wiring safe, accessible technologies to the handyman. Such relation of Law to the greedy interests of power is general throughout the construction industry, and to the uses of all other major technologies.

14. THE GROWTH of large, dense cities is isomorphic to the development of centralized political control: their populations are more manipulable, psychologically and physically. Now urban population density and authoritarian bureaucracy escalate in runaway feedback, heading for the explosive crisis already visible in the progressive breakdown of the physical and social systems of New York City. In such a meta-stable ecology, one element of the dynamic is the protection of the technology which both makes the cities possible and dictates their forms, by the political and economic power-systems which flourish within them. Thus the skirmishing between dome-builders and building codes is a perfect example of how the decentralization of power comes into conflict with its organization into centralized forms. For a decentralized, mobile population, which radical housing technologies make possible, does not lend itself to systems of centralized control. Free up the codes! Power to the People!

EXTENDING THE DOME, IN SUFFICIENCY AND SOCIETY

15. AT A COMMUNE, near Mount Shasta, they are building a methane generator for the thirty light homes among the

trees. It will take their food and body wastes, and yield them gas for heat, cooking, and light—they don't *like* electric light—plus good compost. The technology is adaptable for a one-family dome. Depending upon the ecology of the location, a more ample *energy-independence* could come by supplementing this with generators powered by water or wind; by solar cells, expensive but elegant; or by another technology of sun-energy, like a steam-generator run by a Mylar parabolic reflector. Such sources would feed a sophisticated battery storage system—a moderate investment, until the technology involved gets better. But even now, tied to a small system of reconditioned auto batteries, they could supply current for light, the low-drain appliances made possible by sophisticated electronics technology, and occasional heavier power use, like washing-machine or soldering-iron. Decent steam-generator technology would make heavy-power independence ecologically sound in tended forest land. It is available by dirty tools already, portable and within the reach of group means.

16. I HOPE next spring to build a living model of a family-sized dome which will be a literal greenhouse. Inside, the quality of light will be diffuse, the shadows edged with translucent green from the sunlight filtering through steam, condensed between two-foot-spaced plastic skins, and through the garden whose moist roots bedded in clear perforated cradles will inscribe the dome in hydroponic latitudes and longitudes. And at the pole, sunset will gather distilled in the reservoir below the solar still.

Within the skins of a thirty-foot dome will fit 2,000 square feet of garden, under intensive hydroponic cultivation. Polyethylene breathing panels on the outer skin will exchange new and used air. How many gallons of water cycle through a tomato's growth? Here the water, circulated by hand or power, will be retained within an almost closed system, making the dome desert-suitable. The nutrient input will be regulated, it will come from methane-generator compost plus chemical supplements—supplied by an industry replacing the present life-destroying fertilizer and insecticide industries. No doubt about it, they can be retooled, if production and distribution are freed to follow the people instead of bind them.

Such a large dome-system, perhaps extended by a ground-level closed system using special films to trap solar energy for more rapid growth, if artfully cultivated, could support the people living within it, at least if they were vegetarians. To build and run it for a year would add $500 to basic dome cost. After that, running costs would be very low, at most $200 per year. What living in this relation of completion with the rituals of their food might do to their heads can only be imagined.

17. MYSELF, I LIKE meat. I want to raise sweet fluffy rabbits and kill them with my bare hands, after their idyllic lives in a closed-system hydroponic pasture.

What makes me squeamish is to buy red slabs wrapped in cellophane at the Stupormarket. With meat-processing as with television, we try by technology to divorce ourselves from the wheel of life and death. But it goes on, indifferent to our machineries, which may in turn be used indifferently to extend our perceptions or to numb them. There is choice in the matter. And I don't believe that the alternative to buying a roast of numbness for dinner is to retreat to the purity of stone-ground wheat and stone-age technology.

What is destroying us is not our technology, but the *divisions* we use it to extend. We need to be re*connected*, not divorced from our machines as well, our outered bodies. A plant has its awareness and spirit too, like a rabbit: we cannot live save by killing some principle of life. As long as that's true, good refrigeration makes sense. And so does learning how it operates, as part of the process of healing our divisions. One way for us to begin is to get straight with what we eat. Another is to reconnect with our machines as our extensions, and to become involved with all aspects of our basic life-support technologies, reengineering them as necessary in the process.

18. MANY NOW MAKE such designs. By a variety of technological routes and changes in disposition, the path is being explored toward dwellings which are both adequate and independent as full life-support systems: space, heat,

power, water, food, the whole works; and which grace
and reintegrate the lives lived within them. Taken together
and with a good deal of hustling, and of course illegally,
the technologies now popularly accessible give you or me
the power to experiment with a first version of this Way,
a light technological power-complex adaptable to home in
almost any terrain and sufficiently sunny climate.

19. IMAGE OF DOMES and other eclectic construction
spread out across the land, discrete beneath the oaks,
dug-in on the prairie, sanctuaries in the badlands. Local
materials, local traditions of design, adapted to place and
microculture. Managed forests tended for plywoods and
n-th generation plastics, manufactured in forms for consumer use, and equitably distributed. Even the present
technologies of skin and foam plastics and ferroconcrete
are less wasteful than the structural practices of cities.

We have developed one of mankind's most magnificent
machineries, the chemical industry, toward high art. Understanding the Ways of chemical form and synthesis,
with increasing skill we can tailor molecules to explicit
design needs. So far such powerful art has been turned to
the cheek of Profit, its chiefest accomplishment the creation
of miracle fabrics for shoddy uses. Were profit sufficient,
this great tool could equally be turned to creating a wood/
cellulose-based industry of plastics, by themselves or sys-
tematically biodegradable, whose range of properties would
include and extend those of present-generation plastics.
Who knows, such an industry might become sophisticated
enough to draw its raw materials directly from sun, water
and air—the plants manage, and we are studying their
Ways. But within this century, a first version of an ecologically sound and materially liberating housing industry
is easily possible by changing our technological priorities
and laws.

20. IF OUR SOCIETY felt free to make this change, it
would also feel free to let the manufacture and distribution
of such an industry fall into the natural form of the local
plant operating in balance with the resources of a terrain
and the uses of the population which operates and is served
by it. Such a model points away from centralized control

systems, and toward a scheme of locally centralized facilitation of the needs of freedom. For such industry, the forms of technology still leave room for many ways of cooperation more free than those of our control culture.

21. INVOLVEMENT OF THE community in determining the conditions of life begins in satisfaction of basic needs— in shared local decisions about the plastics plant and its relation with local housing. Universal linkage and free access to computer technology can qualitatively change the handling of social data and enable radical democratization of the information upon which decision-making is based. So can the extending of involvement inward from the plastics plant, perhaps to the point where each citizen's training includes a period of work in local basic support industry, and practical learning from early on in such industrial arts, including their mechanical aspects. Outward from the plant, involvement extends to broader cooperations of local units, as necessary for a process of basic industrial development/manufacture which in turn makes local sufficiency possible. From such a wide popular base of industrial acquaintance and self-determination, intimately linked by high communications technology, priorities and decisions can evolve through democratic systems, rather than through the Yang forms of the economy of profit and ignorance.

TECHNOLOGY AND EDUCATION

22. ALL REAL VISION about technology begins in two facts. Now, for the first time, we have the capacity to feed, house, etc., all mankind, adequately. And we aren't doing it.

Such statements have become trite, irritating, and wearisome to us, perhaps because we're the first people to live within so fully developed a social contradiction about our material circumstances. To the extent that it does not greatly oppress our minds and spirits at the dinner table, we are numbed in the deep reaches.

Until this contradiction is resolved, we cannot be said to have begun to realize the possibilities of social reconstruction opened by our technology. The direction of reconstruction is inherent in its necessary process: a moving toward full, self-determined empowerment, down to the individual level and within, in all of the basic ways necessary to human survival and flowering.

This is also the potential of our present technology. Those who weary early of the possibilities of the Machine should remember that it has not yet been put to the service of making all people materially free, and freeing their imaginations for its furthering uses.

23. So LONG AS there is hunger and the terror of material oppression, the basic style of our culture will be authoritarian. At this point of tension facing our revealed potentials, the cycles of exploitation which define our lives and cripple our energies depend crucially upon the imprisonment of technology. For their survival, our systems of centralized power must limit and control technology in such a way that its potential benefits and empowerment are not realized by most people.

For this to be possible, people must be kept from not only the means but the knowledge necessary to use technology. From this imperative of exploitation spring strong forces which shape and maintain the fragmentary structure of our systems of knowledge and the processes of our specialist education, as well as the unwieldy forms of our industrial machineries. All function to isolate people from technological power. The demystification of technology, the propagation of knowledge and means for its use at the popular level, are essential strategies of struggle against repressive centralized power, and are key to the democratization of technological society.

24. How DEGRADING it is, and how bewildering, to deal with technology in a class society. The refrigerator dies, I kick it, it stays dead. Hey, the refrigerator's dead! Call the refrigerator man. The man comes, his smile is like an ice tray. I have to summon up all my casualness to ask him how a . . . relay? . . . works, and he's not in a mood to chat. We don't learn anything from each other; our transaction is as bloodless as the brick dinner steak.

They divided our functions early, for the sake of the productive economy in its most convenient organization for profit. My sisters learned to invisibly eat their envy at the way my brother and I felt free to experiment with our hands. In high school they offered welding, but I never thought of taking it—nor did anyone I knew who was being prepped for the employment of the mind. Higher education refined their divisions further. I did my undergraduate work in theoretical physics. Our specialized texts helped us encourage each other to feel ourselves a class distinct from those physics majors interested in the experimental face of the art. So I enjoyed my ignorance of their practical skills of electronics and observation; and they refused to learn the funkier language and notation of the electrical engineers, to whom they in turn felt superior.

25. Now, EACH TIME I successfully mess with the carburetor, diagnose the dog, or rig a transistor device to rip off distance phone calls, I get a surge of the peculiar freeing energy that comes from transcending the limits, and hence the condition, of my social class. The state is more than one of empowerment: it has a sharply existential edge.

In our organization around the uses of systematic knowledge, from physics to psychology, each technology is divided into its aspects, and each aspect is assigned to a class of people whose identity it defines and shapes—the essence of Megamachine. The profile of one's relations with the major technologies, productive and other, determines one's caste uniquely. To practice an out-caste technological skill opens one to all the qualities common to the caste(s) "owning" that skill. (A gross example of the process: you can't get on a motorcycle without experiencing a flood of images from films and advertisements.) In a culture in which people know themselves by what they can do, the inward effect is of an opening of the identity. What you know about your capacities and potential becomes unknown, and broader. You enter the livening state of the Nameless.

Now Karen is helping my younger sister learn to drive. She who was always so fearful of machines, now so ripe in her changes for road-freedom, to move under her own power to visit her distant friends and follow her desire on the beaches.

26. ESSENTIAL TO THE repression of change is our cul-

ture's great mystification about technologies. In our mythology, civilization and its technologies—physical and political—are so complex that no one can understand many of the means which determine his life-conditions, or share their practice or control. Each is made mysterious, its power kept from common distribution. Nor is the mystification innocent: it functions in the service of social control. With the physical as with the social technologies, to be ignorant is to be manipulable, and to be unempowered is to be subject to control by outside and greedy forces. Because I don't know how to repair my car and "haven't the time" or capital for the right tools, the auto companies buy laws and the government to guard the waste of production and the earth in deliberate obsolescence.

27. IT IS ESSENTIAL to understand that our relationships with technology need not be as fragmentary as our culture has determined them. Anyone can learn to rebuild a car. The principles of the lightbulb, the laser, and the sun are simple and deep, and open to view: God is not secretive. How can I put it, with the resonance of vision in these stiff words? I believe it's possible for each person to comprehend all the essential technologies of our present lives; and, given the means and need, be able to master any in its use. And I think that any large vision of humanity's reintegration through social reconstruction must include this vision of pan-technological literacy and competence, and in fact depends upon it.

28. WHAT HINGES HERE, on this face of technology, is our image of man. The mystification that the ways of the Machine are arcane and difficult, and few are suited to them, stands against the image of man as a creature whose impulse is toward the embracing of All, whose capacities are larger than his tools, and whose future is open. Against the backdrop of our age, this image is not a "rational" one. It requires an act of faith to project. For by the technological mystification, as by the political, your mind is left unable to grasp what has been done to it and how your imagination has been castrated.

Like the political mystification, the technological one begins to break only through new experience and changed behavior. The walls are thin now, and it's possible for many individuals to transcend significant limits of their technological condition. But our culture's mystification will not be broken until each citizen's education is reformed, in content and process, to enable him to participate fully in our technologies, and their material forms reshaped to suit this.

Such reformation is deeply political. A superficial example: the mystique about black people's lower technical capabilities will not break until the schools and the economy open to integrate them into the technical professions. (Not that black ABM technicians are to be desired per se . . .)

29. AT THE HEART of any new technological politics must lie intimate vision. From my experience, I believe it is possible to raise a child into a new relation with technology, comprehensive, integrated, and harmonious, and that the technology we call technological education can be radically recreated for this. As yet my vision of this is too raw and new to sort out its parameters, I only know that such accomplishment must be collective. But its centering icon is for me the image of our son lying on the floor, discovering geometry with his fist and watching me build above him the butterfly of new geodesic power, while I sing him mantras about Plato and the Perfect Forms.

30. WHEN I WAS seven, my mother convinced my father to move out from the urban core toward the edge of country. I grew up in woodsy Fairfax, medium-north of San Francisco. At night the deer wandered down from the oaks to eat our tomatoes, so we pickled them green. During school-time recess, in the freedom bought by my father's riding the growing freeways to work, I went out looking for lizards.

Dad was a Jewish communist, quick with his hands and his rational mind, who taught me to turn over rocks to see what was hidden beneath them. He was also a cityboy intellectual who knew from nothing about houses. We bought into an absolute leaky lemon of obsolete sub-code-standard construction. And over a decade of work and family hassle, rebuilt it from top to bottom. As I went to bed I saw him hunched over the midnight dining table, studying the government pamphlet on how to do electric wiring. And over slow afternoon years helping him I learned to shingle and sheetrock, plumb and stud, and care for the tools that gave us some power to change things. Then I went off to college, to be groomed for the high priesthoods of our age: after nuclear physics I did four years' graduate work in the best mathematics department. In the end, all that saved me was the coincidence of historical contradiction breaking open, and the impulses of my upbringing in a humane Marxism.

31. LOOKING BACK, it is obvious and astounding how my experience with housing shaped my young life, defined the broader House into whose shapes I grew during the critical years from seven to sixteen.

What was imprinted in me was less fragmentary than the practical opening of many skills, and deeper than a sense of the necessities of craft. I learned in action that I am as Man is, a tool-using animal, and that the ways of technology are open to learning and use: that I am capable, and thus basically empowered. And the process of my learning was precisely this: I watched and questioned and imitated a person who was himself good at learning, and who was learning an ordered set of things in a new context and in response to necessity. It was essential for the depth and way I was affected, that he was not a specialist of skilled routine, but an amateur learning newly and rawly, in trial and failure.

The experience also developed my senses of structure, form, and process, more deeply and organically than the schools ever dared attempt. For the re-building of a house engages productive energies in grand and minor cycles of destruction, beginning, ordering and completion, around elemental needs of survival and grace. A grown man now, writing this I recognize how, like anyone, I have come to conceive the task of social reconstruction, the Rebuilding of our House, in terms of the child-metaphors of my most intimate learning, of leading the copper river up from the foundations to flower into light.

I was fortunate to have shared a relatively complete experience of transformation in relation to housing. I wonder how the experience of growing up in a succession of anonymous tract homes produced by unseen hands, or in the dying cities, emptyhanded, shapes people's root conceptions of social reconstruction and its possibilities.

32. MY EXPERIENCE WITH housing wasn't all harmonious: we carried on our culture's tortured heritage. The women did not share the building save in the customary indirect ways; so my mother hassled with the continual mess of construction and my sisters grew with their hands' powers Mandarin-bound. My parents, for all their politics and warmth, acted out the icon of conflictful division programmed into our culture: man as provider and doer, whose peace is the action of work; woman as manager of the home unit and environment, whose peace is work's termination and whose standards are shaped—even more than his, perhaps because of her relative technological impotence—by the consumer economy of over-use. Thus even within our family developed the bad politics of a scene in which users are at the mercy of technical specialists, and in which the priorities of construction aren't determined by the builders.

Nor were priorities so determined beyond the home: much of our labor to bring things up to code was functionally unnecessary. And even though Dad was a labor journalist who covered the construction trades and well understood the politics of the codes' obsolescence, he never thought seriously of cutting more than a hidden minor corner illegally. In part, his docility came from his unsureness in a still-new sport, and the inaccessible investments of capital and time which experiment in it required. But mostly it came from his being in this, as in all ways of his conduct save the political. essentially obedient to the laws and mores of our authoritarian systems, out of fear.

33. WHEN THE IMPETUS of collective political action freed me from the university, it was to pursue learning differently. My experience as a student and young teacher, in and out of the technological orbit, led me to study afresh how people learn what they need, and how to restructure education about this, as essential to social change. Through the lens of this study, looking back only recently over the

stuff the tides of poetry bring up and leave on the beaches, I discover this image of how I learned at my old man's hands.

Even flawed, it seems to present an essential icon for the way in which education—the process of learning the full wheel of our technologies, material and other—may be reconceived, as a process of continual regeneration, of beginning again. Its Way is learning to learn by the light of example, of competent learners learning newly. Its medium is growing participation in a shared task, of rich form and completion and metaphorical substance, organized around real needs and broad in its human dimensions. Its working-out can begin at any point in human space, our lives, where technology faces upon major needs.

This isn't the whole recipe—there's the matter of more harmonious Ways of authority and control, and in general the transition away from a Yang-tyrannized educational process, and many other matters which I try to treat in my book *On Learning and Social Change*. But even from these few principles, it is clear that to remake (technological) education is to remake our lives, radically and comprehensively, into a context in which the young grow surrounded by example of experiment and risk in transcending our condition.

> So pick up that hammer,
> pick up that gun,
> pick up the flute,
> let's have some fun.

DOME CODA

34. Now I CROUCH in my outlaw dome, writing these notes under butterfly wings that redden with the smog-hyped sunset, while Karen builds the shed into a crafts-room. Perhaps a shade more liberated than our parents—if so, in part by new technology and social conditions, in part by an effort of the will. I bring water to the bamboo, which grows to shelter the dome from the street and with luck will grow over the top before the city inspectors take to cruising with the fleet of helicopters now proposed for

the police. We have given up on the government, we are becoming guerrillas of life in an America of death, outlaws in the technological wilderness. Let me tell you, there is nothing like standing under a helicopter as it swoops down to begin its gassing run to inspire one with new vision. Most young people I know who want to *use* technology would cheerfully rip it off from any institution they could, and some manage to.

35. IF THE NURSERY survives, the ferns will grow through their cycles of frond and spore above our son's bed, refreshing his air, and generations of waterdogs will pass through their larval stages in the vinyl-cupped ecology drawn from the local ponds. I'll get someone to rip me off a good microscope, strong enough to watch their sperm dance and to penetrate the nuclei of our flesh, and we'll learn some things.

And I will tell him the fairy tales of our age. How each life, plant or animal, grows from a word in a language which within my lifetime we've started to learn to read and to construct. And how his someday children may live in houses written from this genetic language in a Yin script: full living creatures, exquisitely adapted to live in symbiosis with man and supply his needs of space and shelter, temperature and food, water and clothing. Taping a jury-rigged oscilliscope onto bean-sprouts, we'll study how different music or anger in the room changes their electrical moods, and dream about how Man and House will feel about each other.

And if the building inspector comes, that too will be a lesson our son will someday understand.

At the Poetry-Reading

Constance Urdang

Hᴇ has taken on the look
of one of his early poems.
The spiky beard and wild disordered eye
Repudiate iambics.

Over obstinate bones
He wears the hair shirt of his chest, and
A single pulsing syllable
Like a clubbed fist.

Inside a cocoon of stanzas
His calves are knotty as a mountain-climber's.
He is pale as a collier from working in the pits.
His feet are sheathed in the leather of his intention.
He plays on silence as if it were an instrument.

Piercing and astigmatic, his glance is blue
As the Asiatic day-flower that noses everywhere
Without shame, even in the neighbor's
Window box. He capers like a shaman

Among the commas and periods, he will have you hanging
From a hyphen! He'll dodge and parry
Like Hamlet—and, at the penult,
With one corrosive, rusty cry
Bound to the sky from the net of your applause.

What I See When I Look Up

John Hollander

WHERE the widening sky
Over the park should have
Cut open the end of
The narrow valley whose
Enclosure I ponder,
Staring up along Sixth
Avenue; where some blue
Washes the thickening
Gray at the end of an
Afternoon; where some gray
Should have spread up from the
Street below to deaden
The bottom of the blue—

The Gizeh Sphinx, her face
The friendly, reflected
Color of declining,
Warm sun, fills up the frame
Of set-back perspective
Space: as if right here,
Near the end of our way,
Amongst vibrant horrors
Buzzing about, she waits,
The old familiar Fear,
Her jocund smile crumbled.
Welcoming, stony arms
Stir, under the warm sand.

Alexandria and Henrietta

Donald Barthelme

Henrietta said: "Once I was a young girl, very much like any other young girl, interested in the same things, I was exemplary. And so forth. I was told what I was, that is to say a young girl, and I knew what I was, because I had been told and because there were other young girls all around me who had been told the same things and knew the same things, and looking at them and hearing again in my head the things I had been told I knew what a young girl was. And so forth. We had all been told the same things. I had not been told that some wine was piss and some not and I had not been told . . . other things. Still I had been told a great many things all very useful and I could see a great many things all very useful but I had not been told that I was going to die in any way that would allow me to realize that I really was going to die and that it would be all over, then, and that this was all there was and that I had damned well better make the most of it. And so forth. I had not been told how to make the most of it. That I discovered for myself accidentally and covered with shame and shit as I was I made the most of it. Then I moved through a period of depression. The depression engendered by the realization that I was beyond the pale, there I was, beyond the pale. Then I discovered for myself and without assistance that there were other people beyond the pale with me, there we were, beyond the pale. Then I discovered for myself and without assistance that there were quite as many people on this side of the pale as on that side of the pale. I discovered for myself and without assistance that the people on the wrong side of the pale were as complex as the people on the right side of the pale, as unhappy, as subject to time, as subject to death. So what the fuck? I said to myself in the colorful language I had learned on the wrong side of the pale. By this time I was no longer a young girl. I was mature."

•

THEORIES OF THE SACRED HEART

LOSS AND RECOVERY OF THE SACRED HEART

CONFLICTING CLAIMS OF THE GREAT CATHEDRALS

THE SACRED HEART IN CONTEMPORARY RELIGIOUS
  ICONOGRAPHY

APPEARANCE OF SPURIOUS SACRED HEARTS AND HOW THEY
  MAY BE DISTINGUISHED FROM THE TRUE ONE

LOCATION OF THE TRUE SACRED HEART REVEALED

HOW THE ABBE ST. GERMAIN PRESERVED THE TRUE
  SACRED HEART FROM THE HANDS OF THE BARBARIANS

WHY THE SACRED HEART IS FREQUENTLY REPRESENTED
  SURMOUNTED BY A CROWN OF THORNS

MEANING OF THE TINY TONGUE OF FLAME

ORDERS AND CEREMONIES IN THE VENERATION OF THE
  SACRED HEART

ROLE OF THE SACRED HEART SOCIETY IN THE VENERATION
  OF THE SACRED HEART

•

Alexandria was reading Henrietta's manuscript.

"This," she said, pointing with her finger, "is inane."

Henrietta got up and looked over Alexandria's shoulder at the sentence.

"Yes," she said. "I prefer the inane. The ane is often inutile to the artist."

There was a moment's hesitation.

"I have been offered a thousand florins for it," Henrietta said. "The Dutch rights."

"How much is that in our money?"

"$266.00."

"Bless Babel," Alexandria said, and took her friend in her arms.

•

Alexandria and Henrietta were walking down the street in their long gowns. A man looked at them and laughed. Alexandria and Henrietta rushed at him and scratched his eyes out. The man howled for help, from his recumbent position, on the sidewalk. Alexandria and Henrietta looked at the blood and eye under their long fingernails.

"What have we done?"

"Forgive us, sir. You look unemployed. Would you like a job?"

Patrick came to live with them. He was to be the cook.

He had excellent references and was also a former Governor of Pennsylvania.

•

As a designer of artificial ruins, Alexandria was well-known. She designed ruins in the manners of Langley, Effner, Robert Adam, and Carlo Marchionni, as well as her own manner. Alexandria was working on a ruin for a park in Tempe, Arizona. The ruin consisted of a ruined wall nicely disintegrated at the top and one end, two classical columns upright and one fallen, vines, and a number of burst urns. The urns were difficult because it was necessary to produce them from intact urns and the workmen at the site were often reluctant to do this. Sometimes Alexandria was forced to lose her temper. *"Hurl the bloody urn, Umberto!"*

Alexandria looked at herself in the mirror. She admired her breasts, her belly, and her legs, which were long and white.

"Now I will go into the other room and ball Henrietta, who is also beautiful."

Alexandria and Henrietta were sweating, in their very large bed. Alexandria's head was between Henrietta's legs and Henrietta's head was between Alexandria's legs. All of the legs were long and white and extremely well-formed.

•

Patrick cooked *Boeuf au Gingembre*. Everyone ate heartily.

•

Henrietta stood up and, with a heaving motion, threw the manuscript of her novel into the fire. The manuscript of her novel that she had been working on ceaselessly day and night for ten years.

"Alexandria! Aren't you going to rush to the fire and pull the manuscript of my novel out of it?"

"No."

Henrietta rushed to the fire and pulled the manuscript out of it. Only the first and last pages were fully burned, and luckily, she remembered what they said.

Henrietta decided that Alexandria did not love her enough.

Nevertheless Henrietta continued to fuck Alexandria

with a dedication, a perseverance, an ingenuity, a fervor, a spontaneity, a wholeheartedness, a passion, a good will, a theoretical grasp, a technical knowledge, an *éclat,* a sincerity, a gusto, a cordiality, a keenness, a dash, a hecticness and zeal beyond anything previously known, in that part of the country.

●

Alexandria was sending a petition to Rome. She wanted her marriage, a dim marriage ten years old to a man named Black Dog, annulled. Alexandria read the rules about sending petitions to Rome to Henrietta.

"All applications to be sent to Rome should be written on good paper, and a double sheet, 8⅜ inches × 10¾ inches, should be employed. The writing of petitions should be done with ink of a good quality, that will remain legible for a long time. Petitions are generally composed in the Latin language, but the use of the French and Italian languages is also permissible.

"The fundamental rule to be observed is that all petitions must be addressed to the Pope, who, directly or indirectly, grants the requested favors. Hence the regulation form of address in all petitions reads: *Beatissime Pater.* Following this the petition opens with the customary deferential phrase: *ad pedes Sanctitatis Vestrae humillime provolutus.* The concluding formula is indicated by its opening words: *Et Deus . . .* expressing the prayer of blessing which the grateful petitioner addresses in advance to God for the expected favor.

"After introduction, body and conclusion of the petition have been duly drawn, the sheet is evenly folded lengthwise, and on its back, to the right of the fold line, are indited the date of the presentation and the petitioner's name.

"The presentation of petitions is generally made through an agent, whose name is inscribed in the right-hand corner on the back of the petition. This signature is necessary because the agent will call for the grant, and the Congregations deliver rescripts to no one but the agent whose name is thus recorded. The agents, furthermore, pay the fee and taxes for the requested rescripts of favor, give any necessary explanations and comments that may be required, and are at all times in touch with the authorities in order to correct any mistakes or defects in the petitions. Between the hours of nine and one o'clock the agents gather in the offices of the Curial administration to hand in new petitions and to inquire about the fate of those not yet decided. Many of them also go to the anterooms of secretaries in order to discuss important matters personally with the leading officials.

"For lay persons it is as a rule useless to forward petitions through the mails to the Roman Congregations, because as a matter of principle they will not be considered. Equally useless, of course, would be the enclosing of postage stamps with such petitions. Applications by telegraph are not permitted because of their publicity. Nor are decisions ever given by telegraph."

"Jesus Christ!" Henrietta said.

•

"This wine is piss," Alexandria said.

"You needn't drink it then."

"I'll have another glass."

"You wanted me to buy California wine," Henrietta said.

"But there's no reason to buy absolute vinegar is there? I mean couldn't you look it up in a book or something?"

"I remember that time in Chicago," Henrietta said. "That was a good bottle. And afterwards . . ."

"How much did we pay for that bottle?" Alexandria asked, incuriously.

"Twelve dollars. Or ten dollars. Ten or twelve."

"And afterwards," Alexandria said. "The hotel."

"Has Patrick gone out?" Henrietta asked.

"Yes. He has gone out."

"Where does he go?"

"I have not asked."

"I wonder what his life is like."

"A comedown I don't doubt. Still I think he's doing very well. He's working out."

"He's working out," Henrietta agreed.

"The hotel," Alexandria said. "You were . . . exquisite."

"I was mature," Henrietta said.

"If you were mature then, what are you now?"

"More mature," Henrietta said. "Maturation is a process that is ongoing."

"When are you old?" Alexandria asked.

"I had not been taught . . . how to make the most of it."

"Is this that?"

"I don't know."

"Better than the cordless electric vibrator," Alexandria said, "I can assure you."

•

Henrietta said: "Now I am mature. In maturity I found a rich world beyond the pale and found it possible to live in that world with a degree of enthusiasm. My mother says I am deluded but I have stopped talking to my mother. My father is dead and thus has no opinion. Alexandria continues to heap up indulgences by exclaiming 'Jesus, Mary and Joseph!' which is worth an indulgence of fifty days each time it is exclaimed. Some sayings are worth seven years and seven quarantines and these she pursues with the innocent cupidity of the small investor. She keeps her totals in a little book. She has to date worked off eighteen thousand years in the flames of purgatory. I tell her that the whole thing is a shuck but she refuses to consider my views on this point. Alexandria is immature in that she thinks she will live forever and live too after she is dead at the right hand of God in His glory with His power and His angels and His whatnot and I cannot persuade her otherwise. My father is dead. Joseph Conrad is dead. Now we are going out."

•

Henrietta and Alexandria went walking. They were holding each other's arms. Then they stopped holding each other's arms and began to hold each other's breasts. Alexandria held one of Henrietta's breasts and Henrietta held one of Alexandria's breasts. People were looking at them with strange expressions on their faces. Alexandria moved her hand sensuously with a circular motion around Henrietta's breast. Henrietta did the same thing to Alexandria. They continued walking, under the shaped trees of the boulevard. They were swooning with pleasure, more or less. Someone called the police.

Housewifery

Heather McHugh

I WANT to be whipped again.
Whole day on the floor on my knees
Scrubbing in a strip-tease acid. While men
Sleep nearby, in a room. Dying to please,
Pleased to die, I wait for someone to wake
Up. Grab a strap. Do me in.

Actually outside the day is soft and not
A killer. Children and noises slip
On it without falling. Where have I been.

After the first week things begin to rot
In the sink. Can't be hip
Doing dishes, baby, watching yourself flip
Plates, stacking the rack.
And I wanted to be born black:

I really must be up for a beating.
Somewhere a bedroom door is beginning to slam
Open, they are coming out. Eating
In the kitchen, messing around, saying goddamn,
Dropping up the floor: I can hear the way a cough
Falls on the tiles and I start taking off, I do start taking off.

Already one of them is playing with his belt
As if it were a sweet thought. Already I have felt
The long line of its coming true, and my own coming
And, across my back, my whole life humming.

Soap Opera

Ira Sadoff

Someone is always dying.

The father is always an alcoholic.
The mother hates her children.
A young girl is often raped
by her own brother.
A long-lost brother loses
his memory.

It is always raining.
Everything happens inside.
A close friend has a nervous breakdown.
Complete strangers break up completely
happy marriages.
A wealthy relative has a heart attack.

One man is always strong enough to stand up
against all this. He is taken off the air.

Disease of the Eye

Ira Sadoff

Sometimes I awaken in the middle of the night,
In the middle of my own house, to discover
Some woman has had her clothes in my closet
For years. She has even slept in my bed.

I feel like a child in an old movie,
Asking myself where have I been. A film
Covers the eye, and I can only recount events
Out of sequence, in a haze. This is not clear

Enough. It is as though I were a doctor
Looking into my eyes with a strange
Light, chasing the pupil into an endless tunnel
Which is not endless. The pupil shrinks

Like a schoolchild who does not know
The answer. I demand to know everything
Below the skin. Who is the stranger sleeping
In my hands? What does a wife mean at night?

Something strange is going on
In my bed. I ask my wife, "Who is this man
You married?" She answers, "He has eyes that run
Behind the lid." For this ailment

The doctor recommends the following:
Cover the eyes with a cold compress of hands.
The stranger will disappear. The lights
Will dim, but you will know where you have been.

Love Scene

Robert Coover

LIGHTS COME UP *on an empty stage. A young man and young woman enter separately right and left, stand opposite each other across the stage, hands at their sides, heads down, preferably at some distance. They are dressed simply, the man perhaps in shirt and slacks, the woman in blouse and skirt. They show no expression whatsoever throughout the entire performance—neither enthusiasm nor sullenness, neither excitement nor disgust, neither belligerence nor boredom. Their movements, while relaxed and natural, are minimal and reveal nothing. After a pause, they both raise their heads slowly until their eyes meet. They regard each other awhile, then begin moving toward each other, taking one or two steps before they are interrupted by an amplified voice. This voice is resonant, rich, capable of all sorts of mood shifts. It can come from anywhere in the auditorium, but preferably from somewhere above the actors.*

VOICE: (*breaking in abruptly*) Hold it! Hold it!

The man and woman stop, look toward the voice source.

VOICE: (*gently*) Uh, that's not quite the idea, kids. You know. It's what makes the world go round, light from heaven, that sorta thing. The sacred flame. Magic in the air and every dream comes true, right? I mean, you're not picking out a can of sardines in a supermarket, there's something happening here, and you have to project that somehow. That Lord-I-can't-stand-it-I'm-gonna-die feeling, know what I mean? All right, so let's back up there now and take it from the beginning.

They step back, take their former positions, heads down,

91

hands at their sides. After a brief pause, they lift their heads slowly until their eyes meet. They gaze at each other a moment and seem about to move forward again, when they are again interrupted.

VOICE: No. No, you still don't have it. What can I tell you? It's very important how we get started here, we don't just lock tired eyeballs and set out, team. You've gotta get something of the old spiritual fire in it, the life of man, the fatal shafts, remember? That jolt of recognition: this is it! Whoopee! A new thing! Never before! Music starts to play! The world stops turning! Okay? Now, give it another whirl there.

They step back once more, lower their heads, pause, then raise them slowly until their eyes meet.

VOICE: Hunh-unh.

They glance up toward the voice source, listen.

VOICE: (*calmly, helpfully, but more authoritatively*) I don't like to interrupt, but you're not—what can I say?— you're just not turning things on. We're doing a romance. Golden dreams. When you look up there, we need the sounds of trumpets. Hearts beating, thumpety-thump. Joy unspeakable and full of glory, got it? All right, one more time.

They lower their heads, then raise them slowly.

VOICE: (*with gathering irritation*) No, no, no, *no!*

They lower their heads, listen.

VOICE: This is a discovery! a revelation! Don't any of these words *mean* anything to you? Ecstasy! outa nowhere! wham-bam! first sight! bluebirds singing, goddamn it! roses in bloom! Come *on*, now!

They raise their heads slowly.

VOICE: (*exasperated*) STOP!

They glance toward the voice, listen.

VOICE: Whatsamatter anyhow? (*Pause.*) Okay, look, here's

the story. Crowds of people. Thousands of stupid people. Every day. And just nothing. You couldn't care less. Am I right? And then, suddenly, out there, on the streets, or maybe in the meadow, across the meadow, or on the bus, in the choir, it doesn't matter, wherever you'd like, across the bar, on a castle drawbridge, you name it: there's this one face. And POWEE! It's magic, it's a message, the world turns green, or pink, whatever, angels sing, there's sunshine everywhere, and bells ring, that kinda scene—okay: take it!

They lower their heads, pause, raise them slowly to stare again at each other.

VOICE: (*snappishly*) You call that ringing bells? Jesus.

They look down.

VOICE: *AGAIN!*

They raise their heads.

VOICE: No, no, no, no, *NO!*

They lower their heads.

VOICE: You're just not making it! You're just not getting me there! I want fire! I want zap! I want desperate under-takings! When you look up and connect, I want the place to *rock!* Come on! Dreams come true! Flames in the night!

They raise their heads slowly.

VOICE: (*angrily*) Goddamn it, NO!

They lower their heads.

VOICE: (*more calmly*) I'm sorry.

They look toward the voice source.

VOICE: Look, think of it any way you like, any way that'll help. You've always wanted a red wagon, right? They tell you that you can't have a red wagon. It's the only thing you want in the whole world and you can't have it. And then, you wake up Christmas morning, and there, under the tree, there it is: a red wagon! Can you feel that? Okay, again now!

They lower their heads, pause, then raise them slowly, meeting each other's gaze.

VOICE: Look, forget the wagon, that was a mistake.

They look down.

VOICE: Let's see, maybe you could try being somebody else. Would that help? What if you were, uh, lemme think, let's say, Paris and Helen, how about that? Let's do the Paris and Helen thing. Greek columns. Ships at sea. Bearded philosophers in the marketplace. Nice bodies running around in togas, or maybe nothing but laurel wreaths, and Paris and Helen. Paris has never seen this girl before, right? And then, suddenly: there she is —ZINGO!

Pause.

VOICE: You don't feel that. Mmm. What about Abelard and Heloise? No? The Brownings? Uh . . . hey, look, I got it! You're Adam and Eve, why not? That's easy! Right! Adam and Eve! So we got the garden, the trees, very lush, are you with me? The glad season. Summer morn. Ripe for exploits and mighty enterprises. Yeah, this is good. You've been buddies, see, but you've never known what the other one was for. You lap the old apple, look up—AHA! Got it? *GO!*

They raise their heads slowly.

VOICE: *STOP!* Stop, stop!

They glance toward the voice source.

VOICE: (*with mounting anger*) I don't want guilt and habit, damn it, I don't want theology—I want EXCITE-MENT! THRUST! IMPACT! Like the man says, I want it filled with fury! Rapt! Inspired! (*With forced restraint:*) You're just . . . you're just there, see, dead in the world, and what a world, it's hopeless, but you look up, and KAPOW! you can't believe it! it's Jesus Christ! it's the Virgin Mary! it's roses of sunshine! violets of dew! it's truth, goddamn it! it's beauty! holy joy! your soul's ambition! your life in death! Oh, god*damn!* Lock on! *Feel* it! *NOW!*

They lower their heads, pause, raise them exactly as before.

VOICE: (*approvingly*) Good! Good! You're getting there! It's starting to happen! Again!

They lower their heads, pause, raise them as before.

VOICE: (*faster*) Come on! That's better! You're in the darkness, you look up: LIGHT! You're in the void, you look up: SUBSTANCE! Again!

They lower their heads, pause, raise them as before.

VOICE: (*high-spirited*) You got it! Don't stop now! We're on our way! Keep it moving! The approach . . .

They take a couple of steps toward each other.

VOICE: *STOP!* Stop!

They stop.

VOICE: (*disgusted, let down*) Why'd you have to spoil it?

Pause.

VOICE: (*grumpily, all the way down now off his gathering peak*) You look like two people out taking a goddamn morning constitutional because some idiot told you it helps keep your bowels regular, for Chrissake! You can do better than that. Now, take it again.

They step back, lower their heads.

VOICE: Skip that shit, we don't have all day, just look up and *move!*

They look at each other, take a couple steps forward.

VOICE: No, no, no! That's not it at all!

They stop, step back, look toward the voice source.

VOICE: Now, listen, let me make it perfectly clear what we want here, team. This is important, so hang in with me. What's happening here, what's about to happen here, is no accident, right? You're not just stumbling into each other, we gotta have the sense of PULL here, ATTRACTION—do you follow me? (*Gradually getting worked up again*): I want that space between you two charged with necessity! alive with COMPULSION! I want powerful inscrutable forces at work! I want transcendence! immortal longings! Are you paying attention? Okay, now you look up, and . . .

They look at each other, take a couple steps forward.

VOICE: *STOP!*

They stop, look toward the voice.

VOICE: (*sarcastically*) Whatsamatter, kids? Shoes hurting your feet? Underwear too tight?

They step back, lower their heads.

VOICE: (*pleadingly*) This is a love scene, gang! This is the biggest thing in your life! This is the biggest thing in history! It's the pleasure that means all the world. It's the sweetest story ever told. It's chasing rainbows through heavens of blue.

They raise their heads, gaze at each other.

VOICE: (*continuing without a pause*) It's the whole goddamn saga of the western world, boys and girls! castles of dreams, finding the grail, music of the spheres! Come on! There's magic in the air, wizards, love potions, and Satan's ass! Every dream come true! Move it! Bee to the blossom, moth to the flame!

They step forward, as before.

VOICE: That's it! Keep going! You had the blues, man, but they're gone, you're moving on! She's the one! He's the one, baby! The anchor! The rock! Come on! Bring it home!

They continue their approach.

VOICE: (*with mounting excitement*) That's right! Good!

Pull! PULL! You're on the way! Over the wastes . . .
through the waves . . . o'er hill and dale . . . up hill
and down . . . moving mountains . . . cleaving masses
. . . You're crossing the great divide! You're reaching
heaven's open door! You're—

*They meet and kiss. This kiss is a simple casual embrace,
hands on each other's arms, mouths meeting—it is instantly
interrupted.*

VOICE: HEY! What the goddamn hell do you think you're
doing!

*They remain together, but part lips and look toward the
voice.*

VOICE: Back up there, goddamn it!

*They part, take a step or two backwards, still looking
toward the voice source.*

VOICE: Okay, that's enough!

They stop, wait.

VOICE: (*a little breathless—even at his calmest, the voice
is now considerably more agitated and excitable than
at the outset*) I'll tell ya when, and not before! You left
out the whole courtship sequence!

They look at each other.

VOICE: Try that shit again, you'll get creamed! I can
destroy you, you little bastards, and don't forget it!
(*He calms. Less threateningly:*) Okay, circle around
there a little bit now. I want it to swing! Ruby lips and
swingin' hips! MOVE!

*Continuing to look at each other impassively, they circle
around, exchanging places, stop.*

VOICE: (*with forced restraint*) That just don't make it,
kiddies. The universe is not exactly standing on its ear.
Come on, now. We gotta have honied lies and the light
fantastic, you understand? We want banquets and
garlands, the stink of roses and the flash of ornaments!
MOVE!

They complete their circle about each other, moving as before, returning to their former positions.

VOICE: (*while they move*) Whaddaya doing? Ya call that the mad whirl? Ya call that ballin' the jack? Oh, that's subtle, that's very subtle . . . (*Explosively:*) But I want REALISM, goddamn it! I want pricks to harden and juices to flow! We're on our way to a fuck not a funeral! Come on, baby! Get some rhythm in that ass, show it to him, whaddaya think ya got one for? Let's have it! Lemme *see* it! Lemme *feel* it!

Whether they have paused or not, they now continue to circle about each other, walking casually as before, watching each other without definable expression, around and around, always keeping the same distance.

VOICE: (*without a pause*) I want tension! vibrations! a living space! heat! harmony! mysticism and melodrama! the feast of reason and the flow of soul! Whaddaya think you're here for? Come on! Good times are comin'! I want the world turnin', fires burnin'! I want appetite and cruelty, joy and devastation! You're swinging now! But it's not crazy enough! Get some grace in it! Get some evil! Glory! I wanna see tempests and torments, sin and suffering! (*Feverishly:*) Okay! Now! Home! GO!

They stop and kiss, as before.

VOICE: HOLD IT! . . . Too soon!

They stop kissing, look toward the voice.

VOICE: (*still very excited, but repressing it*) Back it up!

They step back to the circling distance, still watching the voice.

VOICE: (*with forced calm*) We're rushing it, gang. We gotta do more here to prepare the way, or we'll lose it. Here's where we make it or break it. *This* is our story, not the rest of it, kiddies, we invented tragedy and it happened right here, let's not mock it. We're making it too easy. Not just attraction, remember, but resistance, too. Push, pull, push, pull. Got it? You want it and you don't want it. You're excited and you're scared. You're on the make, but you like it being alone. Go on. Try it now.

They look at each other and begin to circle again, as before.

VOICE: (*continuing*) You know how good it's gonna feel, but it's probably gonna hurt, too. Sensations sweet and all that, but the stink of death as well, the storm of terror. Joy and desolation. Bewitching grace and a sickness full of woes. Push, pull. Push, pull. Are you with me? You gotta have it. But the whole world's watching. You don't care. Everybody in the church is shocked. Everybody in the tavern. Not in *here*, they say. But you can't wait. Lips like a honeycomb, mouth smoother than oil! Yum! Keep it up! Secret trysts! Forbidden gardens! A little tra-la-la, there! a little Blue Danube, moonlight and madness, thick skirts and the flash of nimble ankles, hard thighs, snow-white bosoms, manly brows! Damn it, get some fire in it! Hunt! Flee! Why can't you make it go? (*With gathering gloom:*) What's the matter with you? What's the matter with me? It's always worked before, why isn't it working now? Have I lost it? Has it come to an end?

Pause, while the couple continue to circle silently about each other, round and round.

VOICE: Try the allegorical thing. Love embracing death. The east and the west. Black and white. How about that, kids?

They glance toward the voice source; then, continuing to circle, watch each other, as before.

VOICE: Right, black and white, that oughta be good for something. She's black, you're white. He's a buck nigger, sweetheart, you're a poor little tight-ass white child. Always got things going before, why not now? It's the princess and the blackamoor. Hah! That thing he's got'll split you wide open, honey! She's old mother night herself, boy, fulla sweet delirium and disease! Smell that black stink? Smell that white corruption? Goddamn it, if we got time, if we hurry, maybe you can even go down on each other! (*With gathering excitement:*) Oh yeah, this is pretty, this is primeval, this is depravity and virtue! Unh-hunh, we're getting there now, we are on our way! This is the soul searching for body, conscience terrorized by the gonads! This is night and day, team! sun and moon! yin and yang! Oh yeah! Get ready now! Oh boy! This is beauty and the beast, order and chaos, ego and id, we're up to our ass in it, *feel* it! God and the Devil! youth and age! terrific! the intrinsic and the extrinsic! Zap! Powee! It's a seduction, gang! fight it! grab it! resist! It's man and society! zero and infinity! yeah! time and space! will and necessity! hot shit! it's war and peace! master and slave! *the beginning and the end! SYNTHESIZE!*

They stop circling, step forward and kiss, as before.

VOICE: (*at a high pitch, very excited, very frustrated, coming down hard*) No, no, no, no, no, no! (*Nearly crying:*) Oh, goddamn!

They part lips, look toward the voice source.

VOICE: You're not licking envelopes! You're not checking for fever! *You're in love!*

They kiss again.

VOICE: *LOOK AT ME!*

They part lips, look impassively toward the voice source.

VOICE: I'm telling you! This isn't some greasy old habit, you guys, this is brand new! Can't you get that? This is Columbus at the edge of the world! Goddamn it, if you're about to fall off the damn world, you're gonna *feel* something! This is man in space! This is the soul at death's door! This is a fantastic first encounter with reality! You got that?

They kiss.

VOICE: (*continuing*) I mean, like wow! it's all shock and transfiguration! the backwards look toward the primitive terror! the leap in the dark! the thrust into truth and nature! You've never been there before, you—

Pause.

VOICE: You *have* been there before, haven't you?

They part lips, look up toward the voice source.

VOICE: You bastards.

Pause. The man and woman continue to stare toward the voice, still with no discernible emotion.

VOICE: Well, fuck you. Forget all that, forget all you know, forget it! I said this was new, it's new. Come on! Mouth to mouth, damn it!

They kiss.

VOICE: (*continuing, peaking rapidly*) Eat her up! Suck him dry! I want action! Cruelty! Rape! Deception! Come on! Faster! Outa your minds! Plunging! Grabbing! Damn it, kid, squeeze a little titty there, whaddaya think this is, the Middle Ages? Oh, Jesus Christ, hurry up!

The man puts his hand casually on the woman's breast, as the kiss continues.

VOICE: (*uninterrupted, still accelerating*) Get majesty in it! Panic! Redemption! Possession! Make it weird! This is war! This is the whole enormous evil concupiscence of the fucking universe! Oh shit! Hurry! My God, are ya still *kissing* each other? *JUMP HER, FOR CHRISSAKE!*

They stop kissing. The woman stretches out on the floor. The man stoops down between her legs. They move indifferently, taking their time, as the voice raves on.

VOICE: (*uninterrupted, nearly screaming now*) GO! Oh Jesus! You're children! Naughty! Behind the bushes! Old man! Little girl! You're a priest and a nun! Yeah! Oh! You're Brutus and Caesar! An old lady and her dog! Jesus and his Mom! Brother and sister! Oh goddamn! Luther and the Pope! Uf! Joan of Arc and the stake! Ah! George and Martha! In the privy! In the cotton fields!

Foo! On the floor at the Constitutional Convention! Pull on him, baby! Blow him! Bite him! He's death, baby! He's God! He's the General! Oh hurry! Come on, boy, stick it in her! I want blood! I want grandeur! I want the slap of bellies and the roar of—WHAT THE HELL! *YOU STILL GOT YOUR CLOTHES ON, YOU DUMMIES!*

They look up toward the voice source.

VOICE: Get em off! Hurry! I MEAN NOW! *I CAN'T WAIT, GODDAMN IT!*

The man leans back, begins to unbutton his shirt.

VOICE: *Hers,* you bleeding idiot, not yours! Move it, or you're dead! I swear to God, you're dead! Strip him, baby! Go! GO!

The man stoops over, begins to unbutton the woman's blouse. She leans forward and works one of his shoes off. Etc.

VOICE: No! Can't wait! Rip it off! Faster! (*Screaming:*) I'M TELLING YOU—*RIP IT OFF!*

The man glances up at the voice, pauses momentarily, then proceeds to tear the woman's blouse.

VOICE: (*continuing*) Rip! Kill! Oh! Go! Come! Move! Shit! Sorry! Ah! Please—Aaahhhh. . . .

Prolonged silence. The man and woman are still, methodically, routinely, ripping each other's clothes off.

VOICE: (*dully, still a little breathlessly, wearily, with stupefaction*) All right, knock it off, knock it off.

They glance uncertainly toward the voice, pause, rip just a little more.

VOICE: KNOCK IT OFF!

They stop ripping, sit quietly, attending the voice.

VOICE: Get your goddamn clothes on.

They reach for the torn blouse, shirt. They are still essentially impassive, but there is a hint of growing tension.

VOICE: No, never mind.

They hesitate, drop the clothing, sit back.

VOICE: (*coldly*) You're through, you bastards, you know that.

They sit quietly, but glance at each other. A pause.

VOICE: (*not directly on-mike, but as though shouting into the wings*) Bring an Indian on.

Pause.

VOICE: I don't care, a Gook, a Red, the Mafia, Huns, Moors, witches, zombies, pirates, whatever ya got back there! Ya got a spade technician? Okay, a spade technician, I don't give a shit, bring him on!

Pause.

VOICE: Deus ex machina, my ass! I want that nigger out here!

The man and woman draw together, watch the wings.

VOICE: (*still off-mike*) Whaddaya mean, what does it mean? It don't mean a goddamn thing! It's realism, that's what it is! GET HIM OUT HERE!

A man backs out onstage (if not black, alter the relevant references). Like the man and woman, he is dressed casually, plays his part without enthusiasm or emotion. He carries a pistol, awkwardly, as though it's just been handed him. He turns to face the man and woman, who now stand in a crouch, clutching their torn clothing to their breasts.

VOICE: (*dully, on-mike again*) Shoot em.

The black man stands, hands at his sides, looking up toward the voice source. The other two, holding each other, edge away.

VOICE: You heard me. Shoot em, damn it!

The black man looks around for the voice source, then gazes down without emotion at the crouching man and woman. He does not raise the gun.

VOICE: They're all used up. They're not worth shit anymore.

Pause. Three actors, as before.

VOICE: There they are, man, the whole Western world, all that lunacy, all that history, A to Z, shoot em!

Pause.

VOICE: (*insistently*) Come on! Ya got no balls? IMAGINATION RULES THE WORLD, SHITHEAD! *LET EM HAVE IT!*

The black turns to go.

VOICE: (*pleading*) Wait a minute, goddamn it! At least— look, at least just point the gun at em, just that much, for god's sake . . .

The black hesitates, shrugs, points the pistol more or less in the direction of the other two actors. They huddle together.

VOICE: (*flatly*) Bang. Bang, bang. Bang.

The actors glance hesitatingly toward the voice source, then move quietly offstage.

VOICE: Yeah. That's great. (*Fading:*) That's beautiful. (*Distantly:*) That's just beautiful . . .

Lights dim.

A Reunion

> The Cocoanut Grove nightclub burns
> in Boston, Massachusetts, 492 perish.
> November 28, 1942

1.

It was bad.

In the kitchen,
people burned and drifted
in the flames
like pollen on a stalk.

I thought it was from grease
on the stoves.
I remember the cook gagging,
filling his eyes with ice.

We sat in the food freezer
until they found us.
Shivering.

I live with my sister.
She rubs this salve on my hands.
I don't need it, but she would be sad,
I think, to know they've healed.
We have our routines.

2.

I remember the air

got thick, like jelly
on my face;

it crawled in my dress,
a stood hotness.

I woke, a burnt cow.
The third day, the graft
just slid off,
like an orange peel, on the floor.

I had no new skin.

One night one small girl
stepped in our ward by mistake.
She asked our names, bed by bed,
then, last, slowly, she held
her hand to my cheek
and left.
We all asked for mirrors the next day.

3.

All we had were drunken kids.
It just fell on them.

One man walked behind the bar
and poured himself a drink.

Sailors, dancers, everyone swallowed
some heat.
When they got out,
the cold was like a hot stone.
A girl fell, holding the door
for someone else.

There was a force, a power, loose
in there we never caught.
A gift to us,

for part of one minute,
everything we were, and would be,
stood before us, ready.

We were a child,
a family.

4.

You see this scar.

I just stood there
watching them go.

One hot man stood on
two dead women
to get at a window.
I tried to help a woman limping;
she kicked me.
I still toast the brothers
I found that night.

I sell insurance,
and all I know is, I
tell them where I got that scar.
They buy.

Photograph of Rothko Chapel by Balthazar Korab.

Working With Rothko

A Conversation between
Roy Edwards AND Ralph Pomeroy

ON FEBRUARY 27, 1971, the Rothko Chapel was formally dedicated in Houston, Texas. The Chapel, an ecumenical house of worship, was conceived by Mr. and Mrs. John de Ménil, who commissioned fourteen panels from the late Mark Rothko. The panels are housed in an octagonal structure designed by the Houston architects Howard Barnstone and Eugene Aubry. There are three triptychs approximately twelve feet wide and fifteen feet high. They, together with the five remaining panels, are placed against pale gray walls and lighted from above through skylights.

In 1966, a young painter, Roy Edwards, assisted Rothko in the preparations for these huge paintings. He remembers that there were "a couple of paintings" for the Chapel project already in the East Sixty-ninth Street studio when he began (Rothko had begun working on the commission in late summer of 1965), but that one of them—"not as dark, consisting of bright reds"—he never saw again.

Although there was a mock-up of the Chapel constructed in Rothko's studio, the arrangement of the panels—all of them fields of deep color—underwent continuous revision. Completed in 1966, they were kept in the studio until the spring of 1968 when, following a serious illness, Rothko placed them in storage. During this time the design for the Houston Chapel also went through a number of changes, and construction was considerably delayed. If Rothko had lived, no doubt the arrangement of the panels would have undergone further variation during the final installation.

The importance of the Chapel as a work of art is immense. Rothko was one of this country's great painters, and the project, so far, is unique in the United States. One has to look to Europe for comparisons—with Matisse's superb chapel in Vence or with the series of outsized paintings of water lilies by Monet installed in the Orangerie in Paris.

In terms of Rothko's own development as an artist, the Chapel is a kind of climax. For a long time he had been deeply concerned with rooms or "environments" made up of his paintings: the group of related works he installed at Harvard; the sequence of the Four Seasons, intended for the Manhattan restaurant but finally withdrawn; the room of his works in the Phillips Collection in Washington, D.C. In the last year of his life he worked closely with the director of the Tate Gallery in London, designing the look and lighting of a room especially created to house the nine paintings he had given to that museum.

Several of these "series" are made up of closely-toned, dark-hued canvases in which light seems muted or "turned way down," like the darkening sky just before rain. Their deep color—a whole range of reds (plum, wine, crimson, blood), often combined with black, brown, or gray—is characteristic of Rothko's art as is its exact opposite—high, brilliant, sunny color, a blaze of yellows, pinks, oranges, greens, and blues. The dark side—Rothko's visual equivalent to, say, the awesome "OM" heard in the Malabar cave, in A Passage to India—*is the side shown in the Houston Chapel.*

In the final years of his life Rothko was working on yet another sequence of related paintings—all variants of black and gray—in which sharp white borders appear for the first time in his art.

This interview was taped in June, 1970, several months after Rothko's death.

RALPH POMEROY: How did you happen to get into this thing with Rothko?

ROY EDWARDS: One night in class [at the Art Students League]—my teacher Stamos asked me if I knew how to stretch big canvases. "How big?" I said. "Fifteen feet." I said, "Well, I could try." And he said, "If you want to work for Mark Rothko, give him a call at this number."

So I called him up and went over to see him the next morning. My first impression, when he opened the door of the studio, was of these two huge eyes peering around the doorway. I went inside. We sat down but he didn't really talk very much. He just looked—with those eyes. He asked me what I was doing, how long I'd known Stamos, if I'd ever worked with large paintings. I said, "Not that big, but I think I could learn." For some reason he said, "Okay. Why don't you start immediately?" Like that day he had some things for me to do. So I was there for about an hour sweeping up or something like that. I started working the next day. My first impression of Rothko was that he was something of a Bavarian clockmaker—very careful and slow and precise. All his movements were like thought-out beforehand. He seemed to know exactly where he was at. We got into the work right away.

POMEROY: The stretchers were already built?

EDWARDS: Yes.

POMEROY: Lou Sgroi?

EDWARDS: Lou Sgroi stretchers. I'm a little vague on the size because they ran from twelve feet in width to fourteen to fifteen feet in height, but I may be off a little bit. You know, the dimensions were different on several of the pictures. But it was really quite mechanical. We set up a platform with horses and large pieces of plywood, laid the stretchers on top of that. Then we'd roll the canvas out, cut it, put the stretchers on it—

POMEROY: What, unprimed duck?

EDWARDS: Unprimed duck, cotton duck. I think it was from Belgium or someplace like that. I don't think it was made here.

POMEROY: It might have been linen, then.

EDWARDS: No. Cotton duck. He insisted on it. He didn't like linen. And if there was a piece that had a welt or something running through it, he would discard it. Even though it was a huge piece of canvas to throw away.

It took two days to do a canvas. One day would be spent stretching it; the second day in correcting it. The way we did this was to put the canvas on the floor of the studio and get buckets and sponge mops, wet it down, let it dry . . .

POMEROY: So that it tightened very tightly . . .

EDWARDS: Yes. And if it was too tight, it had to be loosened a little bit. And if there were wrinkles, they would have to come out. So sometimes a canvas would take three or four days. He had several large pictures that he'd already done around the studio, on the walls, and we were always taking them down and putting them on another wall, putting a picture beside it, or shifting up and down.

POMEROY: Were these specifically the Chapel pictures?

EDWARDS: Yes. He had other paintings, of course, that he would look at now and then, and he may have done two or three other paintings in that year. But his work was almost exclusively the Chapel pictures in 'sixty-six. Most of the time was spent not in painting but in contemplation of the painting. Rothko would always say, "An artist has to have a lot of time, free time, to do nothing—to just sit around and let ideas come."

POMEROY: Gertrude Stein said the same thing.

EDWARDS: This is how the work generally went. For a good month we just stretched maybe five or six of these canvases and stored them away in the studio there. In the second month we began the actual painting of a couple of pictures. First the paint was mixed, which was a long process of boiling rabbit's-skin glue and the plastic compound that he used in combination with powder pigments.

POMEROY: Rabbit's-skin glue, like in the old days?

EDWARDS: Yes. He was always reading these books on how to make paintings more permanent. Very concerned with that.

POMEROY: Did he prime? Or was that the prime coat?

EDWARDS: Yes. This took care of both steps, the priming and the painting.

POMEROY: Did he start usually with a dark field or a light field?

EDWARDS: It was a maroon color—which he always referred to as "plum." This is the general background color of all the Chapel pictures. The actual painting of the background was done by Ray Kelly [another of Rothko's studio assistants] and me. The paintings were laid on their sides. We each started from one end and we had to do it like very fast. Rothko would be there supervising, giving commands, very nervous, you know, high-energy.

POMEROY: What do you mean, "on their sides"? They didn't lie flat on the floor?

EDWARDS: No, no, no. They were leaned against the walls.

POMEROY: What did you apply this paint *with*?

EDWARDS: Large brushes. Thick house-painter brushes.

POMEROY: Was the paint thin?

EDWARDS: The paint was very thin. Very thin and watery which we mixed by the bucketful.

POMEROY: Did he mix it himself?

EDWARDS: He picked out the colors and I did the mixing. Because it required hours and hours of stirring. The colors were Alizarin Crimson and black—I can't remember if it was Lamp or Ivory Black. And then this was mixed into the powder paint, which was kind of an Alizarin color.

POMEROY: To begin with.

EDWARDS: Yes.

POMEROY: But he added Alizarin *to* that?

EDWARDS: And black. The oil paint had to be very thinned with turpentine. I would stir and stir and stir and stir so that it wasn't lumpy at all, just like soup, you know. So we took this paint which was in buckets—we needed so much of it—and started painting from each end, while he was giving directions: "You're slowing down on your corner!" Or "Pick up on this end!"

POMEROY: I see what he was doing, though. He was applying washes, and you've got to be very fast with a wash, to make it even. It's like watercolor, same principle exactly.

EDWARDS: But he didn't want it *exactly* even—just enough so it didn't look sloppy. A little bit of play, but not too much. It had to be just right. A couple that we did he didn't like and discarded.

After we painted them he put them up against the wall and looked at them for a few days. You know, the way the drying process would take, the way the color finally sunk into the canvas, and so forth. After several large paintings were finally prepared in this manner, he began laying out the actual *form* on the canvas. This was a large black rectangle running up the height of the canvas, so that the maroon color became its border. This was done in a very precise manner with masking tape. The dimensions of the rectangle were like three inches in from the sides, maybe three feet up from the bottom, and five or six inches from the top. And this was all black. But instead of painting it right away, Rothko had me take large pieces of charcoal and darken in a canvas, so that he could see what it would look like. So this became the sketch for the painting. This was done with a large amount of charcoal dust floating around—I looked like a coal miner after I was through.

POMEROY: I can imagine. On that scale, my God. Were all of the rectangles first charcoaled?

EDWARDS: No. Maybe two or three. It's not that it mattered, because once you do one, you know, you can see it. But he wanted to see the pictures sitting in relation to each other. So we did several. And after this was done, the only thing he did for about a month was just look at them.

POMEROY: The charcoal sketches?

EDWARDS: Yes. I would come in, you know, and maybe clean the studio, and he'd be inside listening to Mozart and looking at the paintings. When he'd reach a decision to make a change in the picture—it would be like to reduce the dimensions of the borders, to increase the black area maybe a half-inch or more.

POMEROY: In other words, it would expand out.

EDWARDS: Yes. Even a *quarter-inch*. I would retape the whole black form a quarter-inch and put in charcoal to expand it.

POMEROY: But these were hard-edge?

EDWARDS: Yes, very hard-edge. Rothko liked to joke about

masking tape being the foundation of modern art. "What would painters do without masking tape, these days?" he'd say. You know, I think these were among the few paintings that he actually ever used masking tape on. He also used it for his last series, which is very different.

This went on for about a month, altering the interior dimensions, in and out. I'd reduce the black form by just brushing the charcoal away, or I'd make it larger. And when he finally made a decision, a fresh canvas was brought out—one that was already primed. The dimensions were put down with masking tape—and I mixed the black paint and he painted the interior form. This was done with his scaffold. The picture was laid on its side again. And he started at one end and worked across. He did all the black forms himself.

POMEROY: But utilizing masking tape?

EDWARDS: Yes.

POMEROY: How thick was this paint? Was it opaque?

EDWARDS: It was opaque, but it was very thin. You know, black is opaque even if it is very thin.

POMEROY: But it wasn't a solid black effect, it was full of nuances.

EDWARDS: Yes, very much so. Because the maroon color filters through.

POMEROY: And he used a brush?

EDWARDS: A brush. His brushes were a big thing with him. They felt like velvet, those brushes, because they were very old and they'd been so well taken care of. I would wash those brushes every day after painting. First in turpentine and then in detergent. For about an hour. Washing and rewashing, rewashing, rewashing.

POMEROY: The story was that he used sponges.

EDWARDS: Oh really? For what? For these particular pictures?

POMEROY: Maybe not for these particular pictures, but in general.

EDWARDS: He never used sponges.

POMEROY: I think people misread that spongy quality in his work.

EDWARDS: No, it was all done with brushes. That's the marvelous thing. He had such a *touch* with a brush.

But he didn't like people to see him painting. When he was doing these black forms, naturally my curiosity would get the better of me, so I would sneak in and sit there and look. And soon he would sense that someone was there, turn around, and say, with the brush upraised, "Get back in there and find something to do!" But I always found a way to get back in for a couple of minutes, just to watch him. It was marvelous. He always wore this old paint-splattered hat to protect his head.

POMEROY: Like a fedora . . . like a Jewish gentleman's hat.

EDWARDS: Yes. So this went on for about another two months. It all seemed to go very fast. I was with him only for a period of six or seven months working on these pictures—but he'd already thought out his conception for the series during the previous two years, so that he knew exactly what he wanted to do, and the actual painting was the only thing left to do. As each painting was completed, we'd set it up on the wall, and he would look at them again and call people in to look at them. He was constantly doing this.

POMEROY: Did he have any favorites?

EDWARDS: Stamos was one of his favorites. Who else? Motherwell came to the studio a few times. Gottlieb. Dore Ashton. Bill Rubin . . .

Every day there would be someone coming to the studio to look at the pictures. You see, in a way Rothko presented a very insecure image of himself as a painter, but I don't think he was at all. He took things in such a measured way—such a precise way—he must have been sure of each step, even though it was small.

POMEROY: So, in other words, none of this frantic gesturing associated with Abstract Expressionists.

EDWARDS: Not with these pictures, but sometimes with others. And then it was all kind of a pose, I think. With these pictures—he knew exactly what he was doing.

POMEROY: Did he set up the whole sequence?

EDWARDS: Yes. Let's see. There's one, two, three, four . . . I think there are four major walls. And on three of them there's a triptych with three panels.

POMEROY: Same size?

EDWARDS: Same size. But the interesting thing about the triptychs is that with at least one of them the middle painting is a maroon blank; there's no black form. Also, it's slightly raised in relation to the other two panels. So actually when it's against a wall, it becomes a shaped canvas. This idea of the blank came one day. We had it on the wall, the blank canvas, and the other two paintings were beside it. Stamos came up for lunch, and Rothko asked him, as he would ask almost anyone, "Well, what should I do with this?"

POMEROY: What a question!

EDWARDS: "What can I do now?" And so Stamos said, "Nothing. Leave it as it is." And Rothko—his head went back, his eyes opened into saucers—

POMEROY: This was the blank, nonimage, centralized . . . ?

EDWARDS: Right. And he didn't say a thing. But he sort of became very quiet for a couple of days, very thoughtful. And this is what it became, finally.

POMEROY: What were the other ones like? Were they in four sets of three? Were they all triptychs?

EDWARDS: No. They're single pictures.

POMEROY: Oh they *are*? How many are there?

EDWARDS: God! You know, I don't even know. I mean, there was so much interchanging and things going on that I don't even know.

POMEROY: Because I was told that the original conception was of a symmetrical cross. So there'd actually be four chapels. That would suggest four series of three walls, which would be twelve paintings, but I don't know.

EDWARDS: Well, that sounds about right. . . . They're going to have to bring them in through the skylight. Those huge paintings coming down through the skylight . . .

When the Chapel is finished, Stamos and I are going to go over the details with Mrs. de Ménil. There's going to be a kind of stucco wall with a slight grayed-off color. It's not going to be bone-white—Rothko didn't want that

—it'll look a lot like pale gray, with a little bit of brown in it, maybe. But we're going to look over the final colors for the interior.

It's very strange, but no one knows how the paintings should be placed—except me. Rothko didn't leave any notes at all. And if I hadn't taken measurements from the studio, all this would have been lost. The paintings would just have been placed haphazardly, without any notion of what Rothko had in mind.

POMEROY: Did he tell you to take measurements or did you just do it?

EDWARDS: I did it on my own. He didn't leave any instructions at all. For him the paintings were done, it was a dead issue, he didn't care any more.

POMEROY: When did he finish?

EDWARDS: He finished that year. 'Sixty-six.

POMEROY: So he went back to painting all these pictures that we're now seeing.

EDWARDS: Right.

POMEROY: Which is very strange. Because the myth was that he wasn't painting anything at all.

EDWARDS: He wasn't painting anything *when?*

POMEROY: Except the Chapel. Since whenever he began. No new pictures were exhibited. No pictures were let out—

EDWARDS: Well, he wasn't painting much during 'sixty-six, I know. I didn't see any.

POMEROY: No, but I mean *since.*

EDWARDS: Well that's ridiculous, because as soon as the Chapel pictures were finished, he began bringing out little pictures for me to look at. You can imagine my reaction after working on those huge paintings. He'd bring out a little blue and green picture, set up a fan, bring over a chair, and very grandly, like a prospective buyer, I'd sit down. He'd say, "What do you think of these cool ocean breezes?"

So gradually he got back to his own painting. He was really into it by the time I left. He was doing a lot of things on paper.

POMEROY: In oil?

EDWARDS: Yes. Some are done with acrylics. He began

experimenting with acrylics, but he never really liked them. He liked the fluidity of oil paints, the transparency. Acrylics just have a plastic quality that really doesn't fit his pictures at all.

POMEROY: And they won't maintain their mix. They keep separating.

EDWARDS: And it's very hard to get with acrylics the kind of edges, the softness that Rothko wanted.

POMEROY: But then you saw him again, didn't you?

EDWARDS: Well, off and on, through the next few years.

POMEROY: You did various jobs and stuff. Do you know when he did that strange . . . I mean the most startling picture to me was that white-bordered one I saw in Venice.[1]

EDWARDS: Those were the last pictures. I think he began painting those in 'sixty-nine. And in the space of one year, I think he did maybe thirty pictures or more. Stamos has the best description—he calls them "very Goyaesque landscapes." And I remember Oliver Steindecker [another young painter who worked for Rothko] saying one day that they look like "night on the moon." And they *do* project this otherworldly, complete-lack-of-human-habitation content.

POMEROY: Are they all monochromatic black and gray?

EDWARDS: Black and grays. And white borders. They're very much denser than his previous pictures. While he was doing this series, he also did several pictures that relate to the earlier things, with the floating forms. He did a blue and green painting, and a red painting, which was one of his last. Very, very loose. The loosest thing he probably did in his whole thing. Bright, bright reds. Very strange, seeing that kind of painting.

POMEROY: And no forms?

EDWARDS: No forms. Not like the black and grays.

POMEROY: Is that going to be shown, do you think?

EDWARDS: I would think so; I'm not sure now. I think there are two or three paintings of the last period in the Venice show. So they're going to be shown, but not as a

[1] In July, 1970, the Marlborough Gallery mounted an exhibition of twenty-seven Rothko paintings in the Museo D'Arte Moderna Ca' Pesaro.

group. The Guggenheim wanted to show these paintings as a group and he was against it, as he was against showing anywhere, oh, for the past ten years.

POMEROY: At least.

EDWARDS: He just didn't want to exhibit. But he was working a great deal in the past few years. There is a big misunderstanding which should be straightened out. When people say "this is why he committed suicide, because he couldn't paint any more," I think that this is crap of the highest degree. Because those last pictures—the black-and-gray ones—are some of the most powerful pictures he painted. They're very hard to get into and understand at first. But once you see them in relation to his other work, their evolution becomes normal and natural. They're very powerful and great paintings, in my opinion.

POMEROY: Well, I only saw that one and, without getting too corny, it gave me a shock. Like the last quartets of Beethoven. It had that kind of risk-taking superficially related to all kinds of things that are going on in art—but with that extra thing, which is Rothko.

And when you get into this clean white—which he's *never* done—dead white—it's like silence. Like the intervals in Beethoven when there is no music. That kind of risk. I just got that kind of feeling. It's the sort of typical comparison that critics make. But these things do apply a little bit. For instance a story I know—do you know Harold Paris, the sculptor? He came to see Rothko once, and Harold told me—this fits with your description—there were all these things with borders—the Chapel pictures. And Rothko said, "What do you think?" And Harold said, "They don't look like Rothkos." He didn't mean it negatively, he meant it as a statement about the cliché Rothko. And Rothko looked at him and said, "Thank God."

EDWARDS: This is what he wanted.

POMEROY: And Harold said Rothko was terribly moved. You know, he's an old friend of Rothko's. Rothko was emotional, you know . . . mystical. That's another thing the critics keep saying, there is no mysticism. The hell there isn't. It's loaded with mysticism.

EDWARDS: Well, I think his whole thing is mysticism. Actually Rothko himself played this down. He'd always say, "I'm not a religious man." That bit. Because he didn't want his pictures to be thought of in a religious sense. But I think they're very mystical.

EDWARDS: Do you know who you should speak to? The painter who lived next door to Rothko, Lidov. He's a commercial artist; he's very negative about Rothko and his work. Rothko would see him almost every night—he'd come in and sit with him and talk—almost every single night . . .

POMEROY: Curious. And he didn't like Rothko's work.

EDWARDS: He *hated* Rothko's work. He hates all modern art. He thinks all of it is crap. But for some reason Rothko would see him every night. It was just the security of being there.

POMEROY: Yes. His being next door. Proximity . . .

EDWARDS: I'm sure it could have been anyone.

Does Uranus Know?

William McLaughlin

The Japanese are building a tanker
large enough to carry the whole world.

I wonder how they are to load this bottom
(which must seem like a bottomless pit!).

Archimedes wanted a place to stand; now
his problem must be solved orientally.

Thought of the extravagance might not
stagger me so if I hadn't been briefed

To believe those little people were
merely good imitators. Imitating whom?

When this ship rolls over it will pollute
more than the coasts of continents.

Capsized, the virginal planets will be
fouled with humanity and our importunate

Artifacts. Sinking the Rising Sun was
providing it with its take-off point;

And when America the Beautiful has been
boxed and crated and loaded on board,

We'll say the old German geographers
proved right: the course of Empire

Does drift westward, westward. Who can
save us now? Ah! Do the Russians know?

The World War I Los Angeles Airplane

Richard Brautigan

HE WAS FOUND lying dead near the television set on the front room floor of a small rented house in Los Angeles. My wife had gone to the store to get some ice cream. It was an early-in-the-night-just-a-few-blocks-away store. We were in an ice-cream mood. The telephone rang. It was her brother to say that her father had died that afternoon. He was seventy. I waited for her to come home with the ice cream. I tried to think of the best way to tell her that her father was dead with the least amount of pain but you cannot camouflage death with words. Always at the end of the words somebody is dead.

She was very happy when she came back from the store.

"What's wrong?" she said.

"Your brother just called from Los Angeles," I said.

"What happened?" she said.

"Your father died this afternoon."

That was in 1960 and now it's just a few weeks away from 1970. He has been dead for almost ten years and I've done a lot of thinking about what his death means to all of us.

1. He was born from German blood and raised on a farm in South Dakota. His grandfather was a terrible tyrant who completely destroyed his three grown sons by treating them exactly the way he treated them when they were children. They never grew up in his eyes and they never grew up in their own eyes. He made sure of that. They never left the farm. They of course got married but he handled all of their domestic matters except for the siring of his grandchildren. He never allowed them to discipline their own children. He took care of that for them. Her

123

father thought of his father as another brother who was always trying to escape the never-relenting wrath of their grandfather.

2. He was smart, so he became a schoolteacher when he was eighteen and he left the farm which was an act of revolution against his grandfather who from that day forth considered him dead. He didn't want to end up like his father, hiding behind the barn. He taught school for three years in the Midwest and then he worked as an automobile salesman in the pioneer days of car selling.

3. There was an early marriage followed by an early divorce with feelings afterward that left the marriage hanging like a skeleton in her family's closet because he tried to keep it a secret. He probably had been very much in love.

4. There was a horrible automobile accident just before the First World War in which everybody was killed except him. It was one of those automobile accidents that leave deep spiritual scars like historical landmarks on the family and friends of the dead.

5. When America went into the First World War in 1917, he decided that he wanted to be a pilot, though he was in his late twenties. He was told that it would be impossible because he was too old but he projected so much energy into his desire to fly that he was accepted for pilot training and went to Florida and became a pilot.

In 1918 he went to France and flew a De Havilland and bombed a railroad station in France and one day he was flying over the German lines when little clouds began appearing around him and he thought that they were beautiful and flew for a long time before he realized that they were German antiaircraft guns trying to shoot him down.

Another time he was flying over France and a rainbow appeared behind the tail of his plane and every turn that the plane made, the rainbow also made the same turn and it followed after him through the skies of France for part of an afternoon in 1918.

6. When the war was over he got out a captain and he was travelling on a train through Texas when the middle-aged man sitting next to him and with whom he had been talking for about three hundred miles said, "If I was a young man like you and had a little extra cash, I'd go up

to Idaho and start a bank. There's a good future in Idaho banking."

7. That's what her father did.

8. He went to Idaho and started a bank which soon led to three more banks and a large ranch. It was by now 1926 and everything was going all right.

9. He married a schoolteacher who was sixteen years his junior and for their honeymoon they took a train to Philadelphia and spent a week there.

10. When the stock market crashed in 1929 he was hit hard by it and had to give up his banks and a grocery store that he had picked up along the way, but he still had the ranch, though he had to put a mortgage on it.

11. He decided to go into sheep raising in 1931 and got a big flock and was very good to his sheepherders. He was so good to them that it was a subject of gossip in his part of Idaho. The sheep got some kind of horrible sheep disease and all died.

12. He got another big flock of sheep in 1933 and added more fuel to the gossip by continuing to be so good to his men. The sheep got some kind of horrible sheep disease and all died in 1934.

13. He gave his men a big bonus and went out of the sheep business.

14. He had just enough money left over after selling the ranch to pay off all his debts and buy a brand-new Chevrolet which he put his family into and he drove off to California to start all over again.

15. He was forty-four, had a twenty-eight-year-old wife and an infant daughter.

16. He didn't know anyone in California and it was the Depression.

17. His wife worked for a while in a prune shed and he parked cars at a lot in Hollywood.

18. He got a job as a bookkeeper for a small construction company.

19. His wife gave birth to a son.

20. In 1940 he went briefly into California real estate, but then decided not to pursue it any further and went back to work for the construction company as a bookkeeper.

21. His wife got a job as a checker in a grocery store where she worked for eight years and then an assistant manager quit and opened his own store and she went to work for him and she still works there.

22. She has worked twenty-three years now as a grocery checker for the same store.

23. She was very pretty until she was forty.

24. The construction company laid him off. They said he was too old to take care of the books. "It's time for you to go out to pasture," they joked. He was fifty-nine.

25. They rented the same house they lived in for twenty-five years, though they could have bought it at one time with no down payment and monthly payments of fifty dollars.

26. When his daughter was going to high school he was working there as the school janitor. She saw him in the halls. His working as a janitor was a subject that was very seldom discussed at home.

27. Her mother would make lunches for both of them.

28. He retired when he was sixty-five and became a very careful sweet-wine alcoholic. He liked to drink whiskey but they couldn't afford to keep him in it. He stayed in the house most of the time and started drinking about ten o'clock, a few hours after his wife had gone off to work at the grocery store.

29. He would get quietly drunk during the course of the day. He always kept his wine bottles hidden in a kitchen cabinet and would secretly drink from them, though he was alone.

He very seldom made any bad scenes and the house was always clean when his wife got home from work. He did though after a while take on that meticulous manner of walking that alcoholics have when they are trying very carefully to act as if they aren't drunk.

30. He used sweet wine in place of life because he didn't have any more life to use.

31. He watched afternoon television.

32. Once he had been followed by a rainbow across the skies of France while flying a World War I airplane carrying bombs and machine guns.

33. "Your father died this afternoon."

After Woodstock

Shirley Kaufman

Her face breaking all over
in little pieces standing up shouting
shit man yeah yeah shaking her hair
like feathers in the dark the man
on the screen splits into three
jerking his arms his legs his neck
three heads six hands now squeeze
the cool sound between his fingers
squeeze the snakes out of his guitar
and three round mouths moan love ya
in the mike pressing it like three
women to his lips

        and leather
rocking smooth in front out of electric
funnels   beads

        they slap the seats
they bounce around me break down fences
to the launching pad

        under their plastic
blankets in the rain slide down
the mud laughing mud in your eyes
your ears there lies the future
but you can't get hold of it sliding
and sliding in the mud

        loving
they call it loving
city bodies naked in the pond
nursing babies while the sun
beats time it's bright

and no one's fighting
in tall grass beside the field
they are taking their clothes off
slowly his pants her blouse his
socks her bra the music insists we can
hear it white flesh now the high
notes grow red grow purple
stain my whole mouth like berries
under the sky they are
berries hundreds of thousands
of berries swaying with their hair.

Shall I let my teeth sail out of my head
higher hug the drummer higher
do handstands on my seat higher shall I
tear up my passport and my credit cards
make my own music out of the dead
years amplified higher come back come
back cut my sleeves into fringes
fly

   out of it   suddenly
it's over and the last sound goes
like a stone dropped into water I can't
find it and the last endless garbage
catches fire and the last car
starts down the highway nothing is
certain only it

              happened

                     there.

Sweet Cheat of Freedom

Ursule Molinaro

for John Evans

He had *not* said: No man is truly free, until he has a slave.

No Roman feels free, unless he has a slave: was what he had said. Rather imprudently, perhaps. To the only daughter of his former master, the senator. When the senator had still been his master. Officially as well as *de facto*. Whose only daughter he had tutored for 11½ of her 16 (almost 16½) years.

Had begun to tutor nearly 12 summers ago. After the senator became senator, after the death of his senator-father-in-law. When the new senator had decided (with his newly inherited rank) that he wanted his only daughter to grow up to think like a man. And had acquired a Greek thinking-slave, from Sparta, to tutor her to grow up to think like a man. Like the son & heir-to-the-senate he'd been prevented from having, by whatever it was that he had given to his wife. Who was of better Roman birth than he was. Brought home to Rome. From one of the campaigns in southern Gaul & passed on to his better-born wife, before he became senator after the death of his senator-father-in-law. Before he & his better-born wife began to age.

Before he began to resent his equally (though differently) aging wife. A little more each day. For not aging the way he was aging: rather resentfully; obesely. For cheating on nature. By looking younger (& younger) than the one year that she was younger than he was.

Because of whatever it was that he had passed on to her, perhaps, that was perhaps delaying the natural aging process of her 39- (almost 39½-) year-old better-born body after preventing it from bearing him other children. Cheating him out of a son, after bearing the only daughter.

Who had grown up to resent her mother.

Whose barely perceptible (rather serene) aging the senator's 45-year-old Spartan-Greek thinking-slave liked to attribute to thinking. Which had perhaps been prompted in the mother's mind by whatever it was that she might have heard him say during much of 11½ years of daily dialogue attempts in which he had tried to involve the only daughter.

Who had perhaps resented her mother's almost daily presence, during much of the 11½ years. From the first day on, perhaps. Walling herself in willful stony deafness against whatever it was that he might be saying.

About a little girl, for instance, who chose boredom in the belief that she was choosing freedom.

Who was probably too little to understand that the only true freedom was freedom of thought. Which many grown-ups didn't understand either. Ever. For which one had first to learn how to think. Not necessarily like a man. Or like a Roman. But like a human being. The only true hierarchy being a hierarchy of minds . . .

Some of which were better born than others. Not socially better born, necessarily. Although a comfortable social position (of senator parents) could be helpful, in certain cases. Wasn't always helpful, however. Induced smugness &/or laziness, & subsequent boredom in certain cases.

Some of which arrived in the world better-equipped than others. With a head-start, so to speak. Which made it easier for them to reassemble . . . in detail . . . the knowledge which the gods took away from man in exchange for his first breath.

Man's first breath blew his mind, so to speak. Wiped his memory-slate clean of most of the subconscious total knowledge of life which man shared with the gods up to the moment of his birth.

Continued to share with the gods in his dreams, after his birth.

When his taking shape, his taking on a specific (the human) form restricted his grasp of life as a totality to the human experience of life. To his own personal perception.

Which was his tool.

Which he had to use consciously, every day of his life, in order to understand his relationship to the other specific forms of life around him: other men/ animals/ plants/ mountains/ rivers/ the sky/ the earth.

To understand all of life by means of his own specific life, as he grew. Up. & older. Toward reabsorption by death. When the gods judged by the sum total of his understanding whether he had succeeded or failed.

WHICH FAILED to scale the willful deafness walls of the 4½–5–5½–6–etc.–year–old mind.

Which he continued to try to scale, unsuccessfully, for 11½ years.

Stealthily ignoring 7 to 8 years of boredom-born tantrums.

The subsequent recounting of which . . . by the mother . . . amused the senator.

Until the tantrums gave way to an equally boredom-born, equally deaf passion for verbal disagreement.

Holding over 3,000 monologues. While: the only daughter nudged her listening mother. Tugged at her listening mother. Poked her listening mother. Climbed one of his legs. Kneaded his lap with her toes. Stared into his eyes. Blew into his ears. His talking mouth. Searched between his thighs with outrageous 4½–5–5½–6–6½–year–old directness.

Which he . . . & the listening mother . . . tried not to see. To pay no attention to. On the principle that: what you don't feed cannot live.

On which principle, its positive & its negative applications:

Feeding an affection with attention; a mind with thoughts; a plant with water.

Starving a resentment/ a jealousy by withdrawing your thoughts from the subject . . . or object; an illness/ a tantrum by ignoring it . . .

he continued to talk. While the mother continued to listen. Both conscientiously paying no attention to the only daughter.

Who disrobed, & marched out of earshot. Past the patio

confines of blue-clustering grapes. Into the late-summer muck of the duck pond.

In which she proceeded to roll her 5-year-old nudity until she was pulled out & returned muck-crusted & flailing to the patio. By a weeping girl, a recent slave from southern Gaul, who was anticipating another beating, this one official, administered by the mistress of the house, after an initial unofficial one, administered by painful bruising 5-year-old fists.

Which the mistress of the house had ceased to administer . . . to any of her slaves . . . after listening to one of his early monologues about the nonviolence of true authority.

Which the mistress of the house should perhaps have administered to the muck-crusted 5-year-old bottom of the only daughter, in spite of what she had listened to him say about nonviolence.

About the unruffle-able serenity of a "true" master. Early that summer. During an aromatic morning in a rowboat on the senator's green-mirroring turtle lake. That had lain in seemingly unruffle-able serenity. Dark-brown turtles dropping from the bullrushes like giant bedbugs; ducks & cranes flying crookedly into the air at the almost soundless approach of the rowboat.

Until the vehemence of 4½-year-old boredom finally succeeded in overturning the boat in which it had felt held captive.

The subsequent recounting of which amused the senator to the point of laughter. (Which was one of man's [dubious] distinctions from [other] animals. A distinction the senator thought he shared with the gods.) Although he had very nearly lost:

1 (& only) 4½-year-old daughter
1 27½-year-old better-born wife
1 18-year-old well-muscled Teuton rowing-slave
& 1 33-year-old Spartan-Greek thinking-slave
    in the process.

Whose fault it would have been if all 4 of them had drowned.

For thinking inadequately.

For not knowing how to capture a 4½-year-old attention. From the first day, the first word, on. For capturing . . . & holding . . . the mother's 27½-year-old attention instead.

For not quite daring to take physically punitive measures. Which were not only not in keeping with his nonviolence principles, but also contrary to certain basic considerations of prudence: A slave striking his master's 4½–5–5½–6–6½– etc.-etc.-year-old only daughter. In the presence of the 27½–28–etc.–etc.–year–old mother, who had listened to years of his monologues about the laziness of violence. While he . . . & the mother . . . continued to ignore the growing only daughter's daily growing boredom.

Preferring to praise the excellence of melon marmalade, when the 6½-year-old flayed an entire field of richly ripe melons which they were passing with a frenzied stick.

When he . . . & the mother . . . continued walking. While he continued to talk.

About: "miniature suns, shining from a deep-green foliage-sky."

& about: "the recurrence of the egg shape everywhere in nature. The neuter, still neutral, shape of the fruit/the seed. With its promise of male & female. Before the split into male & female. Into pistil & petals . . . One split in two, & started talking . . ."

& about: "the all-pervading elementary trinity of earth/ water/ air/ recurring in flesh/ blood/ breath; stem/ sap/ green . . ." Etc. Etc. Etc. Etc. Etc. Etc. Etc. Etc. . . . .

Rather than use the frenzied stick on the melon-shaped . . . already blatantly female . . . 6½-year-old bottom.

A subsequent recounting of which . . . by the sore-bottomed only daughter . . . might not have amused the senator to the point of gods-shared laughter.

Might, on the contrary, have prompted the not-amused senator to revise his Greek thinking-slave's Spartan tutoring methods by cutting off the slavish hand that had dared strike his master's only daughter. Or, more simply, to cut off the slavish head, to put a stop to the kind of thinking that led to slaves striking their master's only daughter.

WHOSE INCREASINGLY violent boredom-tantrums were well in keeping with Roman patrician tradition: according to the senator's Spartan-Greek thinking-slave's unrevised thinking.

The same frantic attempts to silence (with screams of childish rage; & later with the screams of victims: of animals, of slaves) the inner voice that was telling them how unfree they were.

Were free perhaps not to listen to their fathers' thinking-slaves, but not free not to listen to the whisper voice inside themselves that kept telling them that they, the proud patricians, the empire builders, the history-makers, were abject menial slaves. To their needs & greeds. To their craving for effect-producing. For constant world-wide attention.

Were more enslaved than the slaves who served them. Who ruled them, by serving them. Might eventually . . . some day . . . start ruling them without continuing to serve them, if the masters continued to ignore their inner whisper voice. Until they'd become unable to ignore the whisper voices of their slaves.

Who were beginning to doubt the self-mastery of their masters. In the different idioms of their different ethnic & social backgrounds. Which their enslaved condition was melting into one language, spoken & understood by all. The language of passive resistance. In echo-response to the suffering inflicted upon most of them by obesely bored masters. Who called their thoughtless (or, on the contrary, their minutely thought-out) cruelties: necessary punitive measures. Healthy discipline. When they themselves lacked even the discipline not to overeat. & dieted by proxy, by starving their slaves . . .

Who had somehow begun to hear what the senator's Spartan-Greek thinking-slave had been thinking out loud for 7 to 8 years. In the course of his (less & less prudent; more & more outspoken) daily monologues.

Which they'd begun to repeat to one another. In the different idioms of their different ethnic & social backgrounds.

WHICH CEASED being monologues, after the suddenly listening 12½-year-old only daughter began to contradict whatever she thought she had heard.

Vehemently.

& to repeat to the senator whatever she thought she had heard that she had contradicted.

Incorrectly.

Not understanding whatever it was that he might have said. (Somewhat more prudently, lately.) About: the importance of understanding, for instance, the relative unimportance, the luxury, of being understood . . .

About (with all due respects) Juvenal's somewhat unfortunate saying that: *mens sana in corpore sano* was the greatest gift of the gods.

Treating mind & body as two separate entities. As though the mind were not part of the body. As much a part of the body as the hands, the feet. When we needed our whole body to think with. Could understand a concept only after we'd felt its applications with our body.

Which was perhaps why Juvenal was so often misunderstood. Hygienically misunderstood, so to speak. Misquoted, as though he had meant to say that a healthy body was the *conditio sine qua non* of a healthy mind.

Which made about as much sense as saying that a broken leg prevented a man from seeing.

Although it might conceivably prevent him from seeing things in places where his broken leg prevented him from going.

Which made the now-14-year-old now-listening only daughter laugh.

Before (or perhaps after) it occurred to her to burn the soles of one of her father's slave girls' feet with hot stones which she'd ordered the girl to heat. In order to understand the concept of pain.

Which made the senator share in the laughter of his only daughter (which both shared with the gods) after she described to him what she had done after what the thinking-slave had said.

Which the now-listening only daughter had perhaps willfully misunderstood.

Was perhaps making a game of misunderstanding.

A GAME in which the senator was perhaps sharing, when he repeated to all of Rome what his Spartan-Greek thinking-slave had *not* said.

For every potentially rebellious slave to hear. & to repeat.

To believe that he had actually said: No man is truly free, until he has a slave . . . After he'd been given his freedom. & a slave of his own.

Whom to set free he was not free enough.

Nor was he free enough to leave Rome & return to Sparta.

Was free enough only to continue living in the small crude house on his former master's grounds in which he had lived for nearly 12 years. Which felt smaller now that he had to share it with his slave. A not-too-bright, not-too-clean girl from southern Gaul whom enslavement had aged prematurely. Sullenly.

Who sullenly practiced . . . on him . . . the passive resistance he had preached.

Who felt further degraded by serving a former slave. A former "equal." Whom she mistrusted, because she'd been told what he had not said, after he'd been given his freedom. Which he had no way of rectifying, since the girl spoke neither Greek nor the language of Rome.

Hardly spoke . . . or washed . . . at all. A sullen slightly smelly presence. That he felt the unexpected temptation to beat, at times, when she kept persistently in his way, in the smaller-seeming crude house.

Which he no longer had any reason or excuse to leave. Since the senator had deemed that his only daughter was well able to think like a man, like a true Roman, at 16; almost 16½. & that his 45-year-old Spartan-Greek former thinking-slave had therefore no further need to think. Out loud. In the listening almost daily presence of the 39½-year-old mother who continued to age barely perceptibly. Serenely.

Who had sent the Spartan-Greek former thinking-slave the jug of wine he had just finished drinking. The dregs of which had the color & texture of slowly drying blood.

Suggestions for Running Amok

Peter Handke

TRANSLATED BY MICHAEL ROLOFF

FIRST run through a cornfield.
Then run through rows in an empty concert hall.

Then, at the end of the football game, try to get back in the
    stadium through the main entrance.

When you step out on the street are you capable of having
    only *presence of mind?*
When you have stepped out on the street are you capable
    of being only *active?*
Once you have reached a decision are you capable of reach-
    ing no *other* decision?
Are you capable of distinguishing not among particulars
    but only among movements? not horizontals but only
    perpendiculars, nothing human but only softness?
Are you capable of *everything?*

Where do people gather? — People gather where other
    people have gathered.
Where do people gather? — In front of newspapers on dis-
    play.
Where do people gather? — In front of traffic lights.
Where do people gather? — In front of bank counters.
Where else? — In front of show cases when the display is
    being changed.
Where else? —
Around two rabid dogs.
Around spot-remover salesmen.
In front of hotel doormen who've stepped out on the street.
Under awnings when it suddenly begins to rain.

It has begun to rain. — It's not raining hard enough yet.

Where are you going? — First I turn over the fruit cart and

wait until enough children have gathered to pick up the fruit.

And then? — Then I announce the happy news at the street corner and wait until enough people have gathered.

And then? — Then I wait until enough people have gathered to form a lane for someone to run through.

And then? — Then I play dead and leap up when I hear enough people calling for a doctor.

And then? — Then I get people to bet on how many will fit into one car and wait until the car is crammed full.

And then? — Then I wait in the lobby, preferably of a high-rise building, and wait till the elevator reaches the lobby.

And then? — Then I advertise a tour and wait until I have assembled a minimum number of tourists.

And then? — Then I publicize a competition where every participant wins a prize and wait until the first participant asks to collect his prize in person.

And then? — To the telephone booths.

And then? — To the sightseeing tour.

And then? — To the department store escalators.

And then? — To the railway station at the end of the holidays.

And then? — To the observation towers.

And then? — To the resort towns.

And? — Highway exits.

And? — Favorite haunts.

And? — Mountain passes when the sun is bright and hot.

And? — Park benches during lunch hour.

And then? — Suburban windows at supper time.

And first of all? — First of all I engage a single person and wait until enough people have gathered around that individual.

"In other words, you use the first frightful moment to make sure that there will be a second moment of fright, and the second frightful moment to make sure of a further moment of fright, so that you, since you yourself, of course, are free of fright, will always be one moment of fright ahead of them when they are just beginning to recover from their last frightful moment, for which you were responsible, while they were still recovering from the initial moment of fright, so that finally the moments of fright become legion."

And how?

To make short shrift. Don't fuck around. Kill 'em off. Finish
   it up. Get it over with.
"Don't let anyone count, not even to three."

And to top it all off?
And to top it all off I spare someone to carry on the tradition.

Sometimes

D. F. Petteys

SOMETIMES it's just like a thumbprinted film
spider-webbed with scratches from jerking off
the sprockets of a thousand projectors,
the stag-party movie blurred by bad light
and worse acting, heroes having a hard
time keeping erect, no one having any
fun—the old story where they keep coming
to the same awful room, the red-hot French
maid at the service of anyone at all
on her moments off, each one coming to
get whatever it is he thinks he wants,
scratching at her door, nervously clearing
his throat and sliding in, only to be
interrupted by more new arrivals
until they're hidden all over the place,
under the bed and behind the armchairs,
in the closet and even out on the balcony!

Some Reflections on the Ontology of Film

Stanley Cavell

SIGHTS AND SOUNDS

WHAT IS FILM? I want my answer to define the medium in which those objects have been made that I think of as movies, moving pictures. The beginning of an answer is given in the two continuously interesting and, for me, most useful theorists of the subject I have read. Panofsky puts it this way: "The medium of the movies is physical reality as such." [1] André Bazin emphasizes essentially this idea many times and in many ways: at one point he says, ". . . cinema is committed to communicate only by way of what is real"; and then, "The cinema . . . [is] of its essence a dramaturgy of Nature." [2] "Physical reality as such," taken literally, is not correct: that phrase better fits the specialized pleasures of *tableaux vivants*, or formal gardens, or Minimal Art. What Panofsky and Bazin have in mind is that the basis of the medium of movies is photographic, and that a photograph is *of* reality. If to this we add that the medium is one in which the photographic image is projected and gathered on a screen, our question becomes: What happens to reality when it is projected and screened?

That it is reality that we have to deal with, or some mode

[1] Erwin Panofsky, "Style and Medium in the Moving Pictures," in *Film* (ed. Daniel Talbot), New York, Simon and Schuster, 1959, p. 31.

[2] André Bazin, *What Is Cinema?* (trans. Hugh Gray), Berkeley and Los Angeles, University of California Press, 1967, p. 110.

of depicting it, finds a surprising confirmation in the way movies are remembered, and misremembered. It is tempting to suppose that movies are hard to remember the way dreams are, and that is not a bad analogy. As with dreams, you do sometimes *find* yourself remembering moments in a film, and a procedure in *trying* to remember is to find your way back to a characteristic mood the thing has left you with. But, unlike dreams, other people can help you remember, indeed are often indispensable to the enterprise of remembering. Movies are hard to remember the way the actual events of yesterday are. And yet, again like dreams, *certain* moments from films viewed decades ago will nag as vividly as moments of childhood. It is as if you had to remember what happened *before* you slept. Which suggests that film awakens as much as it enfolds you.

It may seem that this starting point—the projection of reality—begs the question of the medium of film, because movies, and writing about movies, have from their beginnings also recognized that film can depict the fantastic as readily as the natural. What is true about that idea is not denied in speaking of movies as "communicating by way of what is real": the displacement of objects and persons from their natural sequences and locales is itself an acknowledgment of the physicality of their existence. It is as if, for all their insistence on the newness of the medium, the anti-realist theorists could not shake the idea that it was essentially a form of painting, for it was painting which had visually repudiated—anyway, foregone—the representation of reality. This would have helped them neglect the differences between representation and projection. But the first fact about the medium of the photograph (still or in motion) is that it is not painting. (The first fact about the *history* of photography is that this fact was not at first obvious.)[3]

---

[3] Certainly I am not concerned to deny that there may be, through film, what Paul Rotha in his *The Film Till Now* (first published in 1930) refers to as "possibilities . . . open for the great sound and visual [i.e. non-dialogue sound, and perhaps non-photographically visual] cinema of the future." But in the meantime movies have been what they have been.

WHAT DOES THIS MEAN—not painting? For us, primarily two things.

(1) A photograph does not present us with "likenesses" of things; it presents us, one wants to say, with the things themselves. But wanting to say that may well make us ontologically restless. "Photographs present us with things themselves" sounds, and ought to sound, false or paradoxical. Obviously a photograph of an earthquake or of Garbo is not an earthquake happening or Garbo in the flesh. But that is not very informative. And it is, moreover, no less paradoxical or false to hold up a photograph of Garbo and say, "That is not Garbo," if all you mean is that the object you are holding up is not a human creature. Such troubles in notating so obvious a fact suggest that we do not know what a photograph is, how to place it ontologically. We might say: We don't know how to think of the *connection* between a photograph and what it is a photograph of. The image is not a likeness; but it is not exactly a replica or a relic or a shadow, or an apparition either (though all of these natural candidates share a striking feature of photographs, namely an aura or history of magic surrounding them).

One might wonder that similar questions do not arise about recordings of sound. I mean, people on the whole would be hard put to find it false or paradoxical to say, listening to a record, "That's an English horn"; there is no trace of temptation to add (as it were, to oneself) "But I know it's really only a recording." Why? A child might be very puzzled by the remark, said in the presence of a phonograph, "That's an English horn" (if something else had already been pointed out to him as an English horn), the way he might be very puzzled by the remark, said of a photograph, "That's your grandmother." Very early, children are *no longer* puzzled by such remarks. Luckily. But that doesn't mean we know why they are no longer puzzled, nor why they were. And I am suggesting that we don't know either of these things about ourselves.

Is the difference between auditory and visual transcription a function of the fact that we are fully accustomed to hearing things that are invisible, not present to us, not present with us? We would be in trouble if we weren't so accustomed, because it is just the nature of hearing that what is heard comes *from* someplace; whereas what you can see you can look *at*. It is why sounds are warnings, or calls; it is why our access to another world is normally through voices from it; and why a man can be spoken to by God and survive, but not if he sees God, in which case he is no longer in *this* world. Whereas we are not accustomed to seeing things that are invisible, or not present to us, not present with us. Or not accustomed to acknowledging that we do (except in dreams). But that seems, ontologically, to be what is happening when we look at a photograph: we see things that are not present.

Someone will object: "That is playing with words. We're not seeing something not present—unless we're hallucinating. We are looking at something perfectly present, namely a *photograph*." But that is affirming something I have not denied. On the contrary, I am precisely describing, or wishing so to describe, what it means to say that there is this photograph here, so that denying my description is precisely denying that this *is* a photograph. It may be felt that I make too great a mystery of these objects. My feeling is rather that we have forgotten how mysterious these things are, and in general how *different* different "things" are from one another, as though we had forgotten how to value them. This is in fact something movies teach us.

Suppose one tried accounting for the familiarity of recordings by saying, "When I say, listening to a record, 'That's an English horn,' what I really mean is, 'That's the *sound* of an English horn'; moreover, when I am in the presence of an English horn playing, I still don't literally hear the horn, I hear the sound of the horn. So I don't worry about hearing a horn when the horn is not present, because *what* I hear is exactly the same (ontologically the same, and if my equipment is good enough, empirically the same) whether the thing is present or not." What this rigmarole calls attention to is that sounds can be perfectly copied, and that we have various interests in copying them. (For example, if they couldn't be copied, people would never learn to talk.) It is interesting that there is no comparable rigmarole about visual transcriptions. The problem is not that photographs are not visual copies of objects, nor that objects can't be visually copied (though such expressions raise questions of their own). The problem is that even if a photograph were, so to speak, a copy of an object, it wouldn't bear the relation to its object that a recording bears to what it copies. For we said that the record reproduces its sound, but we cannot say that a photograph reproduces a sight (or a look, or an appearance).

It can seem that language is missing a word at this place. Well, you can always invent a word. The problem is, one doesn't know what to pin the word on here. It isn't that there *aren't* sights to see; nor even that a sight has, by definition, to be something especially *worth* seeing, hence could not be the sort of thing we are *always* seeing, whereas sounds are being thought of here, not unplausibly, as what we always hear. The problem is that a sight just *is* an object (usually a very large object, like the Grand Canyon, or Versailles; though small Southern children are frequently held, by the person in charge of them, to be sights); or it is an extraordinary happening, like the Aurora Borealis; and what you see, when you sight something, is an object —anyway, not the sight of an object. Nor will the epistemologist's "sense-datum" or "surfaces" provide correct descriptions here. For we are not going to say that photographs provide us with the sense-data of the objects they contain, because if the sense-data of photographs were the same as the sense-data of the objects they contain, we couldn't tell a photograph of an object from the object itself. And we are not going to say that photographs contain the surfaces of objects, for the objects photographed still have their surfaces.

What is missing is, therefore, not a word, but, so to speak, something in nature—the fact that objects don't *make* sights, or *have* sights. I feel like saying: Objects are too *close* to their sights to give them up for reproducing; in order to reproduce the sights they (as it were) make, you have to reproduce *them*—make a mold, or take an impression. Is that what a photograph does? We might try, as Bazin does on occasion, thinking of a photograph as a visual mold or a visual impression. My dissatisfaction with such a line of thought is that physical molds and impressions and imprints have clear procedures for getting *rid* of their originals. Whereas in a photograph, the original is still present, as present in a photograph (mold) as it ever was. Not present as it once was to the camera; but that is now only a mold-machine, not the mold itself.

(2) THIS TAKES US to the second of the ways in which photographs are not paintings. They are not *hand*made; they are manufactured. And what is manufactured is an image of the world. The inescapable fact of mechanism or automatism in the making of these images is the feature Bazin points to as "[satisfying], once and for all and in its very essence, our obsession with realism."

It is essential to get to the right depth of this fact of automatism. It is, for example, misleading to say, as Bazin does, that ". . . photography has freed the plastic arts of their obsession with likeness," for this makes it seem (and it does often look) as if photography and painting were in competition, or that the major painting of the West had *wanted* something which photography broke in and satisfied. So far as photography satisfied a wish, it was a wish not confined to painters, but the human wish, intensifying since the Reformation, to escape subjectivity, metaphysical isolation, a wish for the power to reach *this* world, having for so long tried, and now hopelessly, to manifest fidelity to another. And painting was not "freed" from its obsession with likeness. Painting, in Manet, was *forced* to forgo likeness exactly because of its own obsession with reality; because the illusions it had learned to create did not provide the conviction in reality, the connection with reality, which it craved.[4] One might even say: In withdrawing from likeness, painting freed photography to be invented.

And if what is meant is that photography freed painting from the idea that a painting had to be a picture (that is,

[4] Cf. Michael Fried, *Three American Painters*, Fogg Art Museum, Harvard University, 1965, n. 3; and "Manet's Sources," *Artforum*, March 1969.

had to be of or about something else), that is also not true. Because painting did not free itself—did not force itself to maintain itself apart—from *all* objective reference, until long after the establishment of photography; and then not because it finally dawned on painters that paintings were not pictures, but because that was the way to maintain connection with (the history of) the art of painting, to maintain conviction in its powers to create paintings, meaningful objects in paint. And are we sure that the final denial of objective reference amounts to a complete yielding of connection with reality—once, that is, we have given up the idea that "connection with reality" is to be understood as "providing likeness"? We can be sure that the view of painting as dead without reality, and the view of painting as dead with it, are both in need of development in the views taken of reality and of painting. We can say: Painting and reality no longer *assure* one another.

It could further be said that what painting wanted, in wanting connection with reality, was a sense of *presentness*.[5] Not so much a conviction of the world's presence to us as an acknowledgment of our presence to it. At some point the unhinging of our consciousness from the world interposed our subjectivity between us and our presentness to the world. Then our subjectivity became what is present to us; individuality became isolation. The route of conviction in reality was through the acknowledgment of that endless presence of self. What is called "Expressionism" is *one* possibility of representing such acknowledgment. But it would, I think, be truer to think of Expressionism as a representation of our *response* to this new fact of our condition—our terror of our selves in isolation—rather than as a representing of the world from within the fact of isolation itself. To that extent, it would not be a new mastery of fate, creating selfhood under no matter what odds; it would be the sealing of the self's fate, by theatricalizing it. But apart from the wish for selfhood, and hence the always simultaneous granting of otherness as well, I do not understand the value of art. Or, apart from this wish,

[5] Cf. Michael Fried, "Art and Objecthood," *Artforum,* November 1966; reprinted in *Minimal Art* (ed. Battcock), New York, E. P. Dutton and Co., 1968.

and its achievement, art is exhibition.

To speak of our subjectivity as the route back to our conviction in reality is to speak of Romanticism. Though perhaps the way to understand Romanticism is to see it as the natural struggle between the representation and the acknowledgment of our subjectivity (between the acting out and the facing off of our selves, as psychoanalysts would more or less say). Hence Kant and Hegel; hence Blake secretes the world he believes in; and hence Wordsworth competes with the history of poetry by writing out himself, writing himself back into the world. And a century later Heidegger is investigating Being by investigating *Dasein* (because it is in *Dasein* that Being shows up best, namely as *questionable*). And Wittgenstein investigates the world ("the possibilities of phenomena") by investigating what *we* say, what we are inclined to say, what our pictures of phenomena are, in order to wrest the world from our possessions, so that we may possess it again. Then the recent major painting which Fried describes as objects of *presentness* would be the latest effort of painting to maintain its conviction in its own power to establish connection with reality, namely, by permitting us presentness to ourselves, apart from which there is no hope for a shared world.

Photography overcame subjectivity in a way undreamed of by painting, a way which could not satisfy painting, which does not so much defeat the act of painting as escape it altogether—by its *automatism*, by removing the human agent from the task of reproduction.

And what photography got was not presentness. It got a world, all right; but one which is *past*. One could accordingly say: Photography was never in competition with painting. What happened is that at some point the quest for visual reality, or the "memory of the present" (as Baudelaire puts it), splits apart. To maintain conviction in our connection with reality, to maintain our presentness, painting accepts the recession of the world. Photography maintains the presentness of a world by accepting our absence from it. The reality in a photograph is present to me while I am not present to it; and a world I know and am seeing, but to which I am nevertheless not present, through no fault of my subjectivity, is a world past.

PHOTOGRAPH AND SCREEN

IF THIS ANALYSIS IS VALID, it must be confirmed in the properties of the medium of film itself. Because what I have been saying is useful only to the extent that it extends concreteness. So let us understand what some of the properties of the medium of film are.

And first, let us notice the specific sense in which photographs are *of the world*, reality as a whole. You can always ask, pointing to an object in a photograph, say a building, what lies behind it, totally obscured by it. This only accidentally makes sense asked of a painting. You can always ask of an area photographed what lies adjacent to that area, beyond the frame. This again only accidentally makes sense asked of a painting. You can ask these questions of objects in photographs because they have answers in reality. What does not show in a painting does not exist in that relation to it. We might say: A painting *is* a world; a photograph is *of* the world. What happens in a photograph is that *it* comes to an end.

A photograph is cropped—not necessarily by a paper cutter or by masking, but by the camera itself. The camera crops it by predetermining the amount of picture it will accept; cutting, masking, enlarging, predetermine the amount *after the fact*. (Something like this phenomenon shows up in recent painting. To this extent, these paintings have found, at the extremest negation of the photographic, media which achieve the condition of photographs.) The camera, being finite, crops a portion from a field indefinitely larger; continuous portions of that field could be included in the photograph in fact taken; in principle, it could all be taken. Hence objects in photographs which run past the edge do not feel cut; they are aimed at, shot, stopped live. When a photograph is cropped, the rest of the world is cut *out*. The implied presence of the rest of the world, and its explicit rejection, are as essential to the experience of a photograph as what it explicitly presents. A camera is an opening in a box; that is the best emblem of the fact that a camera holding on an object is holding the rest of the world away. The camera has been praised for extending the senses; it may, as the world goes, deserve more praise for confining them, leaving room for thought.

The world of a moving picture is screened. The screen is not a support, not like a canvas; there *is* nothing to support, that way. It holds a projection, as light as light. A screen is a barrier. What does the silver screen screen? It screens me from that world; that is, it makes me invisible. And it screens that world from me; that is, screens its existence from me. That that world does not exist (now) is its only difference from reality. (There is no *way*, or set of ways, in which it differs. Existence is not a predicate.[6]) The screen, because it is the field of a photograph, has no frame; that is to say, no border. Its limits are not so much the edges of a given shape as they are the limitations, or capacity, of a container. The screen *is* a frame, the frame is the whole field of the screen, as a frame of film is the whole field of a photograph. Or like the frame of a loom, or of a house. In that sense, the screen-frame is a mold, or form.

The fact that in a moving picture successive film frames are fit flush into the fixed screen frame results in a phenomenological frame which is indefinitely extendible and contractible, limited in the smallness of the object it can grasp only by the state of its technology, and in largeness only by the span of the world. Drawing the camera back, or

[6] One will be tempted to say that the screened differs from the actual world in being two-dimensional. But *what* is two-dimensional? The world which is screened is not: its objects and motions are as three-dimensional as ours. The screen itself then? Or the images on it? We seem to understand what it means to say that a painting is two-dimensional. But that depends on our understanding that the support on which paint is laid is a three-dimensional object, and that the description of that object will not (except in an exceptional or vacuous sense) be the description of a painting. More significantly, it depends on our understanding of the support as *limiting* the extent of the painting in two dimensions. This is not the relation between the screen and the images projected across it. It seems all right to say that the screen is two-dimensional, but it would not follow that what you see there has the same dimensionality—any more than in the case of paint, its support, and the painting. Shadows are two-dimensional, but they are cast by three-dimensional objects—tracings of opacity, not gradations of it. This suggests that, phenomenologically, the idea of two-dimensionality is an idea either of transparency or of outline. Projected images are not shadows; rather, one might say, shades.

panning it, are two ways of extending the frame; a close-up is a part of the body, or one object or small set of objects, supported by, and resonating, the whole frame of nature. The altering frame is the image of perfect attention. The cinema found early in its history the possibility of *calling* attention to persons and parts of persons and objects; but it is equally a possibility of the medium not to call attention to them, but rather to let the world happen, to let its parts draw attention to themselves only according to their natural weight. It is a possibility less explored than its opposite. Dreyer, Flaherty, Vigo, Renoir, and Antonioni are masters of it.

AUDIENCE, ACTOR, AND STAR

THE DEPTH of the automatism of photography is to be read not alone in its mechanical production of an image of reality, but in its mechanical defeat of our presence to that reality. The audience in a theater can also be defined as those to whom the actors are present while they are not present to the actors. But movies allow the audience to be mechanically absent. The fact that I am invisible and inaudible to the actors, and fixed in position, is no longer something that needs accounting for; it is not part of a convention I have to comply with; the proceedings do not have to make good the fact that I do nothing in the face of tragedy or that I laugh at the follies of others. In viewing a movie my impotence is mechanically assured: I am present not at something happening, which I must confirm; but at something that has happened, which I absorb (like a memory). In this, movies resemble novels, a fact registered by the sound of third person narration itself, whose tense is the past.

It will be felt: "But surely there is the obvious difference between a movie house and a theater which is not recorded by what has so far been said, and which outweighs all this fiddle of differences: the obvious difference that in a theater we are in the presence of an actor, in a movie house we are not. You have said that in both places the actor is in our presence and in neither are we in his, the difference lying in the mode of our absence. But there is also the plain fact that in a theater a real man is *there*, and in a movie no real man is there. That is obviously essential to the differences between our responses to a play and to a film." What that means must not be denied; but the fact remains to be understood. Bazin meets this fact head on by simply denying that "the screen is incapable of putting us 'in the presence of' the actor"; it, so to speak, relays his presence to us, as by mirrors. Bazin's idea here really fits the facts of television, in which the thing we are presented with is happening simultaneously with its presentation. (If, of course, the presentation is live. If not, it is recorded; that is, *preserved*. We are, in being presented with it, referring to it; and we may or may not wish to refer to it again. A film in a can is being stored, *conserved;* it is neither live nor dead, but waiting. We may or may not wish to present ourselves with it again.) But in live television, what is present to us while it is happening is not the world, but an event standing out from the world. Its point is not to reveal, but to cover (as with a gun): to keep something on view.

It is an incontestable fact that in a motion picture no live human being is up there. But a human *something* is, and something unlike anything else in the world. We can stick to our plain description of that human something as "in our presence while we are not in his" (present *at* him, because looking at him, but not present *to* him), and still account for the difference between his live presence and his photographed presence to us. We need to consider what is present, or rather, since the topic is the human being, *who* it is who is present.

A first impulse is to say: In a play the character is present, whereas in a film the actor is. But that sounds phony, or false: one wants to say that both are present in both. But there is more to it, ontologically more. Here I think of a fine passage of Panofsky's:

> Othello or Nora are definite, substantial figures created by the playwright. They can be played well or badly, and they can be "interpreted" in one way or another; but they most definitely exist, no matter who plays them or even whether they are played at all. The character in a film, however, lives and dies with the actor. It is not the

entity "Othello" interpreted by Robeson or the entity "Nora" interpreted by Duse, it is the entity "Greta Garbo" incarnate in a figure called Anna Christie or the entity "Robert Montgomery" incarnate in a murderer who, for all we know or care to know, may forever remain anonymous but will never cease to haunt our memories.

If the character lives and dies with the actor, that ought to mean that the actor lives and dies with the character. In fact I think that is correct, but it needs clarification. Let's develop it slightly.

For the stage, an actor works himself into a role; for the screen, a performer takes the role onto himself. The stage actor explores his potentialities and the possibilities of his role simultaneously; in performance they meet at a point in spiritual space—the better the performance the deeper the point. (In this respect, a role in a play is like a position in a game, say third base: various people can play it; the great third baseman is a man who has accepted and trained his skills and instincts most perfectly and matches them most intimately with his discoveries of the possibilities and necessities of third base.) The screen performer explores his role like an attic and takes stock of his physical and temperamental endowment; he lends his being to the role, and accepts only what fits; the rest is nonexistent. On the stage there are two beings, and the being of the character assaults the being of the actor; the actor survives only by yielding. A screen performance requires not so much training as planning; of course both the actor and the performer require, or can make use of, experience. The actor's role is his subject for study, and there is no end to it. The screen performer is essentially not an actor at all: he *is* the subject of study, and a study not his own. (Of course: that is what the content of a photograph is—its subject.) On a screen the study is projected; on a stage the actor is the projector. A definitive stage performance is one which, for a time, most fully creates a character. After Scofield's performance in *King Lear,* we know who King Lear is, we have seen him in flesh. A definitive screen performance is one in which a star is born. After *The Maltese Falcon* we know a new star, and a star is only distantly a person. "Bogart" just *means* "the person created in a given set of films." His presence in one of those films is who he is, not merely in the sense in which a photograph of an event is that event; but in this sense, that if those films did not exist, Bogart would not exist, the name "Bogart" would not mean what it does. In that sense, he is not merely in our presence, but we are in his, in the only sense we could ever be. That is all the "presence" he has.

But it is complicated. A full development of all this would require placing such facts as these: Humphrey Bogart was a man, and he appeared in movies both before and after the ones which created "Bogart." Some of them did not create a new star (say, his appearance as the stable groom in *Dark Victory*); some of them defined stars— anyway meteors—which may be incompatible with Bogart (e.g., the one called Duke Mantee and another called Fred C. Dobbs) but which are related to that figure, which may enter into our later experience of it. And Humphrey Bogart was *both* an accomplished actor *and* a vivid subject for a camera. Some people are, just as some people are both good pitchers and good hitters; but so few that it is surpris- ing that the word "actor" keeps getting used in place of the more beautiful and more accurate word "star"; they are only to gaze at, after the fact, and their actions divine our projects. Finally, we must note the sense in which the creation of a (screen) player is also the creation of a character; not the kind of character an author must create, but the kind which certain real people are: a type.

THE ACKNOWLEDGMENT OF SILENCE

WHAT WAS GIVEN UP in giving up the silence of film, in particular the silence of the voice? Why suppose there will be some simple answer to that question, that there was some single spell broken by the sound of the human voice? For the voice has spells of its own.

I think this issue now underlies all the explorations in film I have alluded to. The technology of sound recording soon overcame the actor's stiff bondage to the microphone, and the camera was free to stray again. But the technology did not free it from a deeper source of bondage, namely the idea of synchronization. On the contrary, the possibility of following an actor anywhere with both eye and ear seemed to make their binding necessary. No doubt that source has to do with the absolute satisfaction of a craving for realism, for the absolute reproduction of the world; as though we might yet be present at its beginning.

But there is a further reality which film pursues. I mean the further, continuous reality in which the words we need are *not* synchronized with the occasions of their need, or in which their occasions flee them.

I have in mind not the various ways dialogue can stand at an angle to the life it expresses, or get its power from showing a dot in a summer sea of sociability, which you feel as a peak of depth (Chekhov, Hemingway, Scott Fitzgerald); nor times in which the occasion is in fact past in which you can say what you did not think to say; nor in which the occasion for speech is blocked by inappropriateness or fear, or the vessels of speech are pitched by grief or joy. I have rather in mind the pulsing air of incommunicability which may lap the edge of any experience and placement: the curve of fingers that day, a mouth, the sudden rise of the body's frame as it is torn by the color and scent of flowers, laughing all afternoon mostly about nothing, the friend gone but somewhere now which leads from here. . . . Not just their presence in my present, but the presence of their occasions, the spools of history which unwound only to them then, and then now, which will not reach words for me now, in this occasion, and if not now never. I am not asking for more stream of consciousness. That does not show the absence of words as the time of action unwinds; it floats action and its present in order to give space for the words. I am asking for the ground of consciousness, upon which I cannot but move.

THIS REALITY of the unsayable is what I see in film's presenting of the speaker in forms in which there could be no accompanying speech. Speech slowed to match slow motion sinks into moan and grunt. Speeded human actions become the actions of machines, still intelligible; speech matched to that rises to blurts of twittering. You cannot flash a word into a phrase without altering the phrase; you cannot freeze a word without losing it. The tempo and progression of spoken intelligibility are inexorable. The poetry of poetry finds new breath for the world within that inexorability; it does not, and it does not want to, escape from this condition; poetry shows that we may be up to it. The paces of music have their own inexorability with which, for the time being, to lift speech out of earthly gravity: melisma puts the word in slow motion, but continues the surrounding world as its rod and staff; the soprano's high dominant freezes her word and her world for their descent into one another. The possibilities of moving pictures speak of a comprehensibility of the body under conditions which destroy the comprehensibility of speech. It is the talkie itself which is now exploring the silence of movies.

A silent movie has never been made. We called some silent after others began to speak; but that was to register the satisfaction of the world's reproduction, as if the movie had until then been specifically thwarted from that satisfaction, as if the actors and their world had been inaudible. But they were no more inaudible than the characters in radio were invisible. The Lone Ranger was no more invisible than his horse or his gun, unless you wish to say that what exists as sound is invisible. But no person or object we could be shown could *be* the ones called into existence by those sounds, though you might be interested to know how the sounds were made. No word we could hear could be the word spoken by that figure of silence. We are told that most silents had to be replaced because his or her voice disappointed our expectations, but that a few satisfied us and crossed the boundary intact. No; no one did; all were replaced, some by themselves. We were universally disappointed. The new creations of synchronized sight and sound were merely powerful enough to distract us from the disappointment, and they deserved to. Now the disappointment is waking again.

Movies, before they spoke, projected a world of silence, as the radio beamed a world of sound. Those who miss serious radio will say that, unlike television, it left room for the imagination. That seems to me a wrong praise of imagination, which is ordinarily the laziest, if potentially the most precious, of human faculties. A world of sound is a world of immediate conviction; a world of sight is a world of immediate intelligibility. In neither is imagination called upon.

With talkies you get back the clumsiness of speech, the dumbness and duplicities and concealments of assertion, the bafflement of soul and body by their inarticulateness and by their terror of articulateness. Technical improvements will not overcome these ontological facts, they only magnify them. Such facts are the tasks of art, as of existence. The advent of sound broke the spell of immediate intelligibility—a realistic renunciation, given the growing obscurity of the world. Then the task of the possibility of synchronization is to discover the poetry in speech.

IT WILL NOT be the poetry of poetry. It seemed at first as if it ought to have been, as if when the filmed world expressed itself in speech it would have the same absolute intelligibility as its exhibition to sight. But every art wants the expression of the world, to speak the being of it directly; and none can simply hand its own powers to the others. The poetry of synchronized speech lies in its being just that creature, in just those surroundings, saying just that, just now. Consistently the best film dialogue has so far been the witty and the hard-nosed. That would seem to be because the lines are fast, or laconic. But such qualities are in themselves not always of the highest interest. They work, I think, because they provide natural occasions on which silence is broken, and in which words do not assert beyond their moment of saying; hence occasions on which silence naturally reasserts itself.

For the world *is* silent to us; the silence is merely forever broken. Poems and music incorporate that silence when they speak the world. Film speech can merely imitate it, backed by the world.

How hard it is to let silence resume, how scary, is registered early in the years of talkies, in *King Kong*. The words are not many, and those which are there are either themselves arty ("It was beauty killed the beast") or delivered as artily as can be. But the bulk of the sound track is continuous Wagnerama, and almost as continuous

screams; you finally feel the film is more afraid of silence
than Fay Wray is of the beast. The whole film is an artless
confession of film: film makers on location discover that a
thing of nature is more wondrous than any film; and when
they trap this nature and bring it back, it is displayed
crucified.[7] Movie music remained in genuine continuity
with its soundless era. It continued to cartoon the emotions
it could accompany, and continued to use that as an excuse
for the general deadening of the pain of silence.

In my experience the most perfect provisions for the
breaking of silence by speech are made in two of the
greatest films on anybody's count. In *Children of Paradise*
Arletty breaks the silent conventions of mime with Bap-
tiste's name, the one word drawn from her with his appearance; later, off the stage but staged by a proscenium
window onto the balcony of a theater, she again speaks
just his name as the window curtain is ripped aside revealing them to one another. The speaking of the word in those
times and at those places collects to itself the fantasies it
expresses and shatters them against the reality it shatters.
In *Rules of the Game* the fact that the triumphant aviator's
first words are over the public radio, to a watching world,
but addressed to the absent woman whose presence is
thereby made cause and accompaniment of his solo flight,
gives his words the power of an opening line of Shake-
speare's.

THERE IS ANOTHER HALF to the idea of conveying the
unsayable by showing experience beyond the reach of
words. It is conveyed by freeing the motion of the body
for its own lucidity. This is not dependent upon slowing
and flashing and freezing it and juxtaposing it to itself over
cuts and superimpositions. It was always part of the grain
of film that however studied the lines and set the business,
the movement of the actors was essentially improvised,
as in those everyday actions in which we walk through a
new room, or lift a cup in an unfamiliar locale, or look

[7] The other day in Harvard Square a graffito was declaring,
"King Kong died for your sins." Was this the idea of an inglori-
ous movie maker? Or have I again missed something which
everyone else knows is common knowledge?

over a menu, or ask directions, or greet a friend, or accept an offered cigarette, or add a thought to a conversation. . . . They could all go one way or another. Our resources are given, but their application to just this new crossroads is an improvisation of meaning, out of the present. These trivial facts take us back into the idea of acting on film. Earlier, I was objecting to calling the subjects of film actors at all. But obviously, whatever they are, they are actors the way any human being is. The ontological fact that actions move within a dark and shifting circle of intention and consequence, that their first significance is that they are ours, and that their fate, like the fate of words, is to be taken out of our hands, and that the individual significance of an act, like that of a word, arises in its being this one rather than every other that might have been said or done here and now—this is the natural vision of film; and in particular, the fact that this condition is fixed, that the circle of action, as of assertion, is inescapable for the body with a soul, fated to the providing and the accepting of meaning.

To act without performing, to allow action all and only the significance of its specific traces, the wound embracing the arrow and no self-consciousness to blunt or to disperse that knowledge—that has been the explicit wish of human action since Kierkegaard and Nietzsche summed up Protestantism and Stanislavsky brought theater into line. Brecht automatically gets an unanticipated version of his wish for the epic in theater and the alienated in acting: not the dissociation of actor and character, but their total coalescence, allowing a dissociation or freeing of action from speech. And not quite the whole wish, not the goal of detached lucidity directly issuing in effective action for change. But then art alone is not going to achieve the changes of consciousness which its own reception also requires. Brecht gets "the turning of the spectator into somebody who just looks on," but without "forcing him to make decisions." [8] But then it ought to be part of epic theater to contain the confrontation of its own continuous failure—that every night we know the truth of our condition,

[8] Cf. "The Modern Theater Is the Epic Theater," in *Brecht on Brecht* (edited and translated by John Willett), New York, Hill and Wang, 1964.

and every day dawns just the same. Not to make this failing palatable; but equally not bitter, because our tongue will adapt to any taste it needs. To make it something we can live with faithfully, in consciousness, and with readiness for the significant detail when it really is ours to act upon. And Brecht gets the vision that everything in the world, other than nature, is a human construction, humanly open to change. And he surprisingly gets the absence of the spectators' "involvement" as in the events on a stage.

For the impact of movies is too massive, too out of proportion with the individual worth of its ordinary instances, to speak politely of involvement. We involve them in us. Not as lines of poetry, which, if they are possessed, work into the metabolism of bone, become part of our structure. Movies enter rather as part of the occasion of their going, to become another fragment of what happens to me, another card in the shuffle of my memory, with no telling what place in the future. Like those childhood memories whose treasure no one else appreciates, whose external appearance is as nothing compared with their unspeakable importance for me. St. Augustine stole a pear; lots of children have. Rousseau got a spanking with his pants down; lots of little boys have. Why seems it so particular with them? But everybody has his stolen pear, and his casual, permanent seductions; if we are to know our lives, those are to be known. Parents are forever being surprised at their children's memories. Some find it amusing or quirky of them to remember such details; some boast, on that evidence, of their child's great intelligence. But all this shows is that the parents do not know what is important to the child; and their amusement and boasting mean that they are not going to try to learn.

Panther

Nicholas Rinaldi

WITH Robert Mitchum I hunt the black cat.
Paw prints in the snow.
He's a big one, but Mitchum is tough.
The horse whinnies.
Indian Joe-Sam is scared.
The snow blows, flakes like silver dollars.

Diana Lynn waits at the house,
her dress buttoned up to her chin.
No one will see her breasts.
Her hair is braided in a bun.
She has the hots for young Harold.

Arthur, the middle brother, is killed—
clawed by the cat.
While Harold digs the grave, Ma lays him out proper.
There is a unicorn carved on the antique bedstead.
At the funeral, Ma throws dirt on the coffin.
Pa is drunk on whiskey.

Mitchum presses on.
I follow along, his shadow in the snow.
Look out for Mitchum: he is burly, crass, power-mad.
But wise.
He knows who the panther really is:
". . . the cause of all the trouble in the world."
A pregnant pause.
"The evil in everybody."

Diana Lynn offers herself to Harold—
"You'll be alone with me, if I lead you by the hand."

He hesitates, then lays her down in the straw.
They don't take off their clothes.

In a cave, Mitchum lights a fire and reads Keats.
"When I have fears that I may cease to be. . . ."
He does have fears.
When he finds the black panther, he runs.
Down the icy slopes of the Rockies.
Panic drives him.
He falls down a canyon.
Dies.

I know now who I am.
I am not Mitchum's shadow.
I am Harold in a mackinaw,
trudging across a mile of snow.
Behind a grove of pines, I shoot the black cat dead.
Diana Lynn is mine.

Joe-Sam has the last word:
"Him devil—black panther."
Ma smiles sweetly.
Pa will never drink again.

In Sydney by the Bridge

Turner Cassity

CRUISE ships are, for the young, all that which varies.
  The aged disembark with dysenteries.
Always, it is middle age that sees the ferries.

  They hold no promise. Forward or reverse
  Impels them only to where what occurs,
Occurs. Such is, at least, the chance of being terse,

  And is their grace. The lengthy liners, fraught
  Sublimely, shrill for tugs. If they're distraught,
That is because the thoughts of youth are long, long
    thoughts—

  Save those of gratitude. The slow, massed force
  That frees them they will cast off in due course,
To learn, or not to learn, the ferries' sole resource:

  How, in the crowding narrows, when the current
  Runs in opposition and the torrent
Claws the wheel, to locate in routine, abhorrent

  For the storm, the shore that makes it specious;
  Where one calls the vicious, curtly, vicious,
And the scheduled ferry, not the cruise ship, precious.

Terry Meets the Lusiads

Turner Cassity

THE low bronze lions lord their English bank,
Succinct Gibraltars of the Hong Kong trading floor;
    The symbol noble but the feline rank,
    As if the perfidies were there, and stank.

    Low temples, on the Macanese shore,
Have for their symbol Fortune in a grosser guise.
    Gautama or the new casino—whore—
    It is the Wheel of Things they bow before:

    Our giddy Empress. Lifting rheumy eyes,
The Buddha, over double chin, cries faites vos jeux.
    The bony croupier, serene, all-wise,
    Draws profit from the path he must advise.

    The Wheel releases whom its slots prefer.
And on the Hong Kong bourse the bank shares fluctuate;
    They ticker-tape an Albion less sure,
    But more perfidious. It will endure,

    At least as Portugal endures. The state
That is the withering away of state, the city
    Uncontinuing, alike await,
    Last chips not yet in place, the turn of Fate.

A Letter to Ismael in the Grave

Rosellen Brown

SOMEBODY once told me I didn't have welfare mothers' eyes.

I. I. I. I. I. Like white is supposed to be made up of all the colors, I is made up of all the words you can possibly say all running together in a circle very fast. It is red and shiny and purple and sweet. A mouthful of I-berries. Here, have some. I want to put it on the mailbox. Use it for my signature. Frame it and hang it on the wall all gold. Put it between my legs in bed at night. Sing it out in church. Show it around like a fat new baby. It's the best baby we never had, the one I made myself, after the children had gone to bed, just before you died.

You know what your sister said to me, don't you. She says it with her pointy finger. Back to the ashes, Cinderella. Now be a dead man's wife the way you were a lost man's widow.

When I was a kid I once walked across the river on the third rail, right next to the BMT. While I was at it in those days making my mama and grandmama jump like fleas, I married you. But I couldn't do that once, like walking the rail, I had to do it and keep doing it for thirteen years. So I fell in the river, my feet in flames.

Does someone always have to get blamed in this world?

The headline was 2 MORE ADDICT DEATHS IN CITY THIS WEEKEND.

What I read was WIFE SAYS SHE DIDN'T KNOW; SAYS SHE

STOPPED KNOWING ANYTHING A LONG TIME AGO. And who gets blamed for that?

You know my friend Nilda. Her husband takes a shot every single day of his life for diabetes, very carefully, so he won't go blind or something, or go crazy. How can it be that another man could use his veins for filthy highways— for alleys, that's what, dark dirty alleys. So they could find you collapsed in the thick black of one of your own ruined veins.

Merciful, merciful. That you died before you had to hock your children's eyes and little toes. Before your pig of a liver killed you instead. Before I sold myself out from under you and cheap, to get money for passage. I am not beautiful, no sir, I know that, but I do not have welfare mothers' eyes. In spite of you.

All right, I said to him. But you know I've got tattoos. Those shadows, those stripes of the El laying over me all these years since you (he, Ismael, my husband!) moved me here. I swear we've got the taste of all that darkness in our soup. You have to look pretty hard even in Brooklyn to find an El that they haven't taken down for scrap-iron and firewood but you worked hard on it and found us one. You couldn't get sunstroke over here if they gave you a million for trying. One time I saw the slats across my friend Rita's shoulders when she was standing down there on the stoop. They looked like those fox furs I used to stare at when I was a kid, the whole fox with the flat shiny eyes I always thought were real, and the long dark stringy tails. Didn't you used to wonder if it hurt them, and look in those live eyes, to be dragged around on some rich old lady's back?

He was looking at me the other day when I thought I was alone, sitting in the kitchen trying to think. And he said he never saw a woman who kept right on existing when her man wasn't with her. I guess I've had a lot of practice from you, with me and never with me all at the same time. But Jesus, to be that way! What are we, frogs who need a swamp to croak about?

The kind of thing I've been so busy thinking is,
Whose fault were you?   But
Whose fault was the you whose fault you were? There's
a girl on the front of the Sun-Maid raisin box holding
a box of raisins with a girl on it, holding a box of
raisins with a girl on it holding

Something new, I heard them talking on TV about what's
called crimes without victims? Do you think there could
be something like victims without crimes? That's what we
all could be, even the kids—victims' victims. Don't laugh.

It had nothing to do with heroes or heroines. But two
people live in a room small enough so their shoulders
touch when they pass—picture it—and don't know each
other's names. One day one of them asks "What's your
name?" and it turns out they have the same name. By accident. "Well," one of them says, "maybe we have something in common. What do you like best in the world?"
She looks at him coyly and says, "You." She smiles because
she thinks that's the right answer. "And what do you like
best?" He thinks for a minute and says, "Me." So they fall
together. It's a tight circle they can both fit into if they get
down on all fours and crawl.

Poor Ismael. When you closed your gorgeous eyes that I
envied, there must have been nothing behind them to look
at. Just dark: your own closed eyes reflected and reflected.

You said I made the children a wall between us, you even
made it seem that was all I had them for. But a wall is
something to lean on when you have to lean, and anyway,
what holds up a house, a roof overhead, if it isn't walls.

I asked you to leave. I threw you out. I left you. But I've
heard about a kind of snake—this is a moreno belief, I think
—that kills you and when it thinks you're dead it sticks its
tail up in your nostrils to make sure you aren't breathing.
If you are, it kills you again. What you used for a tail and
where you went looking to see if I was still alive—I
shouldn't have lay down dead for you so often.

If I ever loved you, even for a minute, then you were my
fault too. I put a check-mark next to you and it wouldn't

rub off. I said sure. I laughed. I said I'm behind you here, give me your footprints—even for a minute. I said we fit.

What did you say to me?

So it's going on. I think of myself, I shine up the me with powder and pink lips and what do I see but a roach climbing like a little trooper up from the baseboard, and what do I think of? Me is like a genie that goes in and out of my toilet water bottle but you are always somewhere around without being called. I paid money I didn't even have to get you a better place in the ground than you ever got me up here, and a woman to say the rosary a full three days, and you're still smoke around my shoulders. I looked at this fat roach that never got sick eating the paint off the walls because there's better things to pick at, and thought how that was you lying next to me in bed—that bed the man from welfare used to say was too big for one and leer at me—and that is still you lying in darker dark and a roach might be taking away your fingers right now for all I know. For all you know.

I know something you don't know.

The priest keeps saying, spreading out his big sweaty hands to calm me down, Now Ismael knows the last great secret, he is luckier than we are. Then he goes and names all the saints whose faces you're getting to see whether you want to or not. But I saw you dying and it was like watching you do something very very private when you didn't see me looking.

It wasn't merciful, I lied, something just got sucked away out of your eyes and when it was gone your cheeks began to collapse fast. But it was more of you than you ever showed me, dressed or naked, cold or hot, sick or sober. It was more.

Now how do I get out from under you. That's what I mean, I'm like one of those women a man died while he was inside of. Had a heart attack or something, you've heard about that. No matter where they take his body, she must always see his shoulders hunkering over her with his eyes wide on her face. I know it. And she thinks it's her fault

too, a little bit, somehow a shadow of the fault, a sniff, a
turn, an ooze of the fault.

The night he came home with me the first time and the
last, Rosa who is your daughter no matter who's in my
bed, came running into the bedroom crying Daddy is a
ghost and he's scaring me. He tried to comfort her but she
didn't even know who he was sitting there wrapped up in
a sheet, and it took me an hour to get her back to bed.
Then all we wanted to do was forget we ever saw each
other, and he got dressed and went home. And I was glad.
If you didn't get Rosa up out of her bed to come running
in there on me just in the nick of time, then I think I did,
with some strong part of my brain that I can't see.

I was planning another getaway when you escaped. Rosa
was at my mother's and Chico was in his first week of
sleep-away camp, and I was going out and get a job, I
thought something on a boat going somewhere out of
Brooklyn, I don't know, but I was standing right at the
threshold, in a way. Singing, singing the whole day how
you weren't going to lock me up from myself the way you
locked me up from you. Then they came and told me they
found you and these little sunbursts of color kept popping
in front of my eyes just like when I drink, dark with rainbow colors. They had to lead me. They told me as though
it was no secret how you'd been robbing me and telling
me stories and laughing at me and shooting your children's
groceries up in your arm and my breasts turned to clean
round skulls that you had kissed in the morning. Somebody,
Julio, said he was surprised I cared so much, I looked so
weak choking on my own blood, and he took me to the
hospital to breathe in the dead air you breathed out, and
I said I don't like to be made a damn fool of, that's all.
And there you were turned inside out in your skin like
one of your own empty pockets and who was the damn
fool then? Julio, the last time I saw him maybe a month
ago, ran his hand down my behind with his finger pointing
like an arrow, and I thought for a second that I might be
free of you. I will tell you without shame I'd like to have
made a bow bent for your dear friend Julio's arrow. But
after he took me to your sweaty bed and showed you to

me stretched out hot with your brain dissolving right before my eyes, I told him to go away. He shames me with
myself.

They took you to the morgue and I had to go and check
you out like some lost package. I was right there when you
died and the doctor knew who I was and you didn't have
to die in the street but maybe I do have welfare mothers'
eyes. So I traded them down at that place, the morgue:
They gave me what was left of you and I gave them my
feet and they locked them in a vault.

Now you see   a widow is a dry well. You always hear
the opposite. But I'll have them too, won't I? Heart's
beetles. Six fat maggots feasting on my tongue that knew
your tongue. I. I. I the stillborn.

Ismael. I wish you were alive, I wish, I wish, so I could
hate you and get on with it.

My Double in a Drama Filmed in France

Herbert Morris

I KNEW you afternoons in railway stations
whose single-track trunk lines run dusty, late,
between one desolation and another,
you in the most ill-fitting uniform
issued by a once-proud Italian army,

sipping a coffee at an outdoor table
with a young girl who wished to be your sister
in a cold, gutted room above the station
for the brief hour before your train's arrival,
or a woman who thought she was your mother.

I knew you by the placement of those hands
before you on the table, hands that sifted
light in them like white bowls in northern windows,
a strange, mild sun lapping the province that day,
blinding the eyes of the piazza's statue,

warming us who were never wholly warm,
teaching us light who had not been taught light.
To the south, rumors of profound defeat
continued circulating through the morning
with the arrival of the dispossessed

by coach and van, their packs slung on their backs,
carpets and mattresses lashed to gaunt horses.
In the confusion, little would seem lost
but the long waiting which became our lives.
I knew you where the dust began to dance,

the roar of cannons, din of mortarfire

suddenly drawing closer in its focus,
the troops of forces called the enemy,
according to reports, reaching the outskirts
by daybreak of that morning we awake

to understand, I think for the first time,
who we are, where the battle has been fought,
in some dim breach that everything depended
not on the reinforcements' late arrival
but somewhere on one's way of saying yes.

That evening, in a room above the station,
absence would sing as sweetly as a presence
on the cold, rusting springs to which it clung,
the dark-haired girl go out to seek a brother,
the older woman sleep with other sons.

The day the peace was signed, when you came home
through the baroque of that shell-battered station
where much of what we dreamt had taken place,
I knew you where the cuff exposed the wrist
and where the collar spoke too much of neck,

where what seemed you and what seemed uniform
walked each distinctly the Italian dusk,
the vast smoke of the last provincial light
filtering through the nakedness between.
I knew you knew the route that rent the night.

Laying Down the Gun

Emile Capouya

I

THE SOUNDEST principle for revolutionaries is to begin
to act at once in the spirit of the more perfect society they
envision. The whole strategy and tactics of a movement
that aims at improving the terms of life are contained in
that principle, and ought always to be referred to it strictly,
as a matter of conscious policy. A revolution that is worth
bothering with at all is one that will allow us to be better
than we can be now; we have to lift ourselves by our boot-
straps to achieve it. We cannot receive it as a gift; we cannot impose it by compulsion. The idea that much can be
accomplished by changing "conditions" is useful only insofar as we remember that we are our conditions, that we
embody them in our actions and in our thoughts. Customary movements of reform proceed on the assumption that
conditions are objective and persons subjective, which
amounts to regarding things as real and people as fictitious.
For that reason the usual patterns of reform achieve, insofar
as they are effective, more ingeniously tyrannical forms of
the abuses they set out to correct. A long process of such
purblind improvisation may indeed result in progress, or
men may be goaded by it into a better view of themselves
and their problems—much of the conscious program of the
Marxist parties has depended upon "gains" and "improvements" that must exacerbate the discontent of the working
class—but this is surely a blundering way to arrive at a
decent human polity.

To state the principle is easy. But only the grossest con-
tingencies or choices offer clear cases for its application.
In theory, everyone understands that if we want peace we

do not try to achieve it by war; if we want freedom we do not make it depend upon slavery. But our history is a tissue of just such policies as common sense, dealing abstractly with the question, would call perverse. The argument of the slave-owners before the Civil War was that a republic of free citizens, gallant, liberal, public-spirited, was possible only where demeaning labor was performed by a special class of helots, a kind of animate machinery. It is plain to us now that the slaveholding South had been impoverished, materially and morally, by the "peculiar institution" to such a point that its defeat in the war was very nearly inevitable. As for the program of achieving peace through warfare, we are at it right now, testifying to that part of us that is still undiluted idiot. It is worth remarking that these examples have a common element that helps to explain how men could possibly embrace the absurd paradoxes they represent: both arise in a context of systematized social violence.

What distinguishes the state from society in general, and from fractions of any particular society, is its effective monopoly of the means of violence. The state has it and employs it; society as such does not. The distinction is important because the idea of society represents the area of more or less voluntary relations in human affairs, while the state represents the area of relations ordered by compulsion. We live in an age in which nearly all societies are governed by states. It was not always so. There are historical reasons that explain why it is so at present. There are reasons, too, for believing that the institution of the state is not necessarily synonymous with civilization—that in fact we have arrived at a historical stage in which the possibility of a stateless society at a high level of civilization can plausibly be envisaged. Nevertheless, the reality we are accustomed to is that of the coercive state, and naturally our imagination is colored by our experience of its institutions. The general context of social relations governed essentially by compulsion—ranging from mild intimidation to outright violence—perverts our judgment in cases like those mentioned earlier, to the point that we are nearly helpless to apply our best insights to our problems.

Even enlightened and well-intentioned men who are

convinced of the validity of the principle that we are discussing—the necessity to act now in the spirit of that polity
we hope our children will attain to—often interpret it in a
way that testifies to the crippling effects of social coercion.
Each man, they say, must act in that spirit all by himself,
within his own family, in the circle of his friends, in those
limited relations he has with other men in his character of
citizen, producer, consumer, etc. His example will spread
by contagion, and when his adherents have grown to be a
majority, the humanly useful revolution will be seen to have
arrived. It is a curious position, remarkable for positive and
negative features that cancel each other out. To begin with,
the insight it expresses is a perfectly true one. Every meaningful change starts in the altered consciousness of individuals. That is the positive aspect of the thesis—it states
the least condition for deliberate reform. Its negative side
is the powerful implication that the only virtue is solitary,
that attempts to be decent *en masse* are a contradiction in
terms. The men who hold this view have been so shaken
by our coercive institutions as to imagine that society and
coercion are one, that wherever there are two persons one
must oppress the other—unless he receive a revelation
from him, as Paul did from Jesus. In consequence they
have become anchorites of the imagination, withdrawing
spiritually from their fellows, as if in flight from a battlefield
to avoid having to kill and be killed. Practically speaking,
this negative side of the doctrine renders impossible that
contagion of example on which it rests its hopes, since it
restricts personal influence to the smallest conceivable
range.

BILLY GRAHAM CALLS upon each of us to become a
Christian, to receive the revelation attested in blood, that
we may see the truth of the Gospel injunctions to charity.
When all the world has done so, salvation will be at hand.
The mighty of the earth are well pleased with this doctrine;
President Nixon has made it, so far as he was able, the
state religion, and given marks of favor to its evangelist.
There is no harm in it from his point of view, because its
form is self-defeating. Mr. Nixon knows that the two
hundred million Americans are not going to receive Christ

as their personal saviour, hold all things in common, and order matters so that the lowly shall be exalted and the mighty be brought low. These psalms and hymns are the appropriate background music for certain earthly crusades carried on with bullets, napalm, and high explosive. In its religious dress, the radical individualists reject the message of Billy Graham, but they cling to their own secular version of it, which is scarcely more threatening to our masters. At bottom, it is a vote of no confidence in mankind, which means either fear or arrogance or both; one can taste in these statements a fastidious shrinking from the common life and a Pharisaical assumption of superior merit. They will let their light shine before men, and those who have eyes to see. . . .

It seems reasonable to imagine, on the contrary, that men can confirm themselves in virtue more readily and more meaningfully in society than in some desert of the mind. If we mean to live our convictions, we must surely have help—unless our convictions are so self-regarding that we can give full effect to them in solitude; and in that case, why do we need to discuss them and urge them on others? Infantilism and cold-heartedness we have plenty of as it is, and they are boring. In the social context, then, since we aspire to be men, what practical interpretation can we give to the principle of revolutionary action?

II

THE DIFFICULTY, at once, is how to transcend a violent society without ourselves falling into violence, how to avoid substituting a more self-righteous tyranny and more prac- ticed, more ruthless instruments of coercion for those we have now. This is by no means a popular view of the problem. The relatively few men and women who under- stand that we are already in the midst of a revolution, and that we must try to influence its direction, are ac- customed to conceive it in terms borrowed from another era, or from contemporary struggles in countries culturally remote from our own. What is called the Old Left is con- cerned with problems that arose in the early and middle stages of industrialization, and with solutions first propounded in those times. The New Left has its attention fixed upon the colonial wars now raging, and the hand-to-mouth expedients of guerrillas, who are taken as models—not only morally, as they often deserve to be, having demonstrated qualities of manhood long disused in our country, but practically, as if there were a special efficacy in close combat. Old and New have their eyes turned elsewhere, away from their own time and country. The one imagines that its scholastic formulas have power over social conditions that have changed beyond recognition in the last fifty years, the other that the necessities of destitute peasants are a school for learning how to deal in this country with the power of the corporate state.

The reason for the guerrilla mentality of the New Left is an odd one, quite unexpected because its logic is emotional rather than intellectual. It must be approached on the bias if we mean to seize it. The immediate cause of the unrest of the young in the United States is not aimless affluence, anomie, or the unavailability of socially constructive or personally fulfilling work. All these conditions—which are very real and very painful—flourished as well in the 1950's, and the young people were perfectly passive. Since that time, without ever becoming quite conscious of the grounds for their attitude, a generation has been raised that has contempt for this society, its government, its sanctions, and its symbols. When these young persons first began to take notice, they observed that the system they found disappointing and irksome on so many counts was the same that was unable to subdue a nation of Asian farmers, or impose its will on the Cuban rebels just ninety miles off the Florida coast. They live in a different world from that of their elders. The world they know is one in which the most prepotent, bullying government of modern times (Mr. Nixon to the legate of the Prince of Peace: "I fly from here to the most powerful fleet the world has ever known") turns out to be impotent to control small, impoverished nations that have a mind to be independent. Contempt for such a government comes naturally to them, and they think it perfectly natural that their government be contemptible.

Older people have a better estimate of the destructive

power of the corporate state, including its power to wage a war of extermination. They understand very well that our rulers have chosen to deploy less than a tenth of our strength in the Vietnamese war, and done little more than frown at revolutionary Cuba. With the exception of a relatively few deranged persons, the citizens who remember the Second World War and how a nation prepares in earnest for armed struggle, are very happy that neither Mr. Kennedy, Mr. Johnson, nor, thus far, Mr. Nixon, has felt moved to play the hero in that way. The military problem of subduing Vietnam, for example, is perfectly solvable. What it requires is full American mobilization, six million men under arms as in the Second World War, with the appropriate accompaniments: full conversion to war production, fixed prices and wages, rationing of gasoline, rationing of food and tobacco. Had we invaded Vietnam with a force of the order that general mobilization can support, the war would have been over—for the way to fight guerrillas is to saturate the entire theater of war with troops. Under those conditions, guerrillas have literally no room for maneuver, and the populace upon which they must depend for supplies and manpower is under effective control. In the case of Vietnam, of course, there would have been a danger of provoking serious countermeasures on the part of the Chinese, as happened during the war in Korea. But it can reasonably be argued that the Chinese intervened in Korea after it was clear that the American government, in keeping with its characterization of the war as a "police action" undertaken on behalf of the United Nations, had not mobilized for a serious fight and probably would not do so. If the invasion of Vietnam had been supported by full mobilization in the United States, the Chinese might very well have abstained from an intervention that would necessarily involve them in full-scale war. It is an odd reflection, but if the United States had actually played in Vietnam the role it advertises to the world, that of the supreme arbiter who will not brook contradiction, its young people would not now think it despicable.

Of course, there are powerful motives that keep our government from playing that role to the hilt: it is disproportionately expensive in terms of the goal to be achieved, and economically and socially disruptive to the point of political unfeasibility. That is the meaning of the colonial wars of the modern period, in which the "mother countries" have had to resign themselves to the loss of raw materials, markets, and outlets for investment because of the political costs of taking the strong measures required to subdue the rebellious colonies. So at bottom the United States has fairly earned the contempt of its children by its policy of doing evil with the left hand only, on a calculation of cost-efficiency. In Vietnam, the idea was to do the job on the cheap. When that turned out to be a strategic miscalculation, our leaders did not want to recognize the fact. They vacillated, one foot on the platform and one foot on the train. They are still doing it. The position is ridiculous, and the youngsters jeer.

As a result of all this ineffectiveness many young militants have become convinced that the American government is weak, and that it cannot defend itself against an armed rising at home any better than it can fight abroad. These young radicals do not know how they have come by this conviction, nor how mistaken is the sequence of assumptions that supports it. It appears to them to be so self-evident that they are puzzled and exasperated by the government's continued existence—and also react in panic at the first steps in the direction of general repression of dissent to be taken by the Justice Department, the police, and the less visible agencies of social control. Just as, never having seen a real war, they cannot conceive that the government has not yet seriously engaged the Vietnamese (though it has exterminated thousands of them), so, never having seen repression and not taking much stock in history, they imagine the routine harassment of radicals now going on to be a kind of Kronstadt, Kristallnacht, and St. Bartholomew's Eve rolled into one. Thus far, only the systematic murder and imprisonment of the Black Panthers looks like serious repression, and I say "only" because it does not compare in scope with the suppression of the I.W.W. after the First World War, when the government and its thrones, powers, and dominations made a clean sweep of a militant organization that had numbered upwards of two hundred thousand during the dozen years that ended in 1917. Not to mention that merely being black makes the Panthers ten times as vulnerable as a white group with the identical program would be. The treatment given the Panthers is in the mores of the country; it is very nearly business as usual.

The very misapprehension that leads radicals to apply doctrines evolved by serious soldiers like Mao Tse-tung and Guevara to a battlefield they never visited, on principles they would not countenance, against odds they would not consider accepting, gives a certain élan to their young admirers in this country. The Old Left in its turn wonders admiringly or fearfully at the militancy of the young—not suspecting that that attitude is based on a mistaken estimate of the state's power to coerce that it could not possibly fall into itself. In fact the judgment of the New Left fluctuates erratically on this point, sometimes imagining that it faces a remorseless juggernaut and sometimes a paper tiger. When the attention of the young radicals fastens upon the violence of the police, the tactics of entrapment by means of provocateurs, and the generally hostile climate in which they may have to stand trial for real or imaginary offenses, their hearts sink, naturally enough, under these pointed intimations of the power of the state. But when it turns to the saga of Castro and Guevara, and to their own government's imbecile helplessness to extricate itself from a war, lost long ago, against foot-soldiers in Asia, then the radicals are led to think that their own tactics have simply not been bold enough, not provocative enough to bring down the braggart, blundering system of power. And they tend to respond in ways that show how very American they are, after all, how imbued with the vulgar romanticism of the dream-factories of Hollywood. The rain of high explosive in Vietnam has a pizzicato echo at home in the bombings—hundreds more than are reported in the official press—by middle-class guerrillas in the name of revolution.

The morality of this artisanal, cottage-industry destruction is not nearly on a level with that of the official violence promoted by our government, but it does compromise enormously the prospects for a revolution that would be worth having. It is precisely when confronted with a question of this kind, when human weakness leads us to condone or embrace a bad policy because we understand the context in which it arises and sympathize with the goal proposed—in this case, the ending of the war—it is precisely at such a time that we have to refer to the leading principle of a decent social revolution: act always in the spirit of the ideal; the means we employ stay with us for a long time, they become part of our character; if they are not consistent with our ends we shall never realize our ends. To discriminate correctly in the face of practical urgencies is enormously difficult, of course. We are men, not machines. In my own case, I know very well that I could summon up more indignation about Leftist violence if it were not Leftist, and particularly if my feelings had not been blunted on that point by the wholesale murder of the Vietnamese people. In the glare of that holocaust it is difficult to focus on the tragic errors of the American militants at home, simply because the scale of their folly is incommensurable with that of the government's mass-produced atrocities. Nevertheless, since some domestic violence proceeds from persons who profess much the same values that I do, I cannot avoid declaring that their actions are incompatible with their aims. We cannot arrive at the reign of peace and liberty through a campaign of small-scale terrorism. A policy of that kind is itself an example of social pathology, and it has more to do with the society we hope to escape from than with the society we hope to build.

SYMBOLIC ACTIONS SUCH as bombings—often at the instigation of police spies—are more likely than not to be counterproductive even on the crassest calculation of practical efficacy. The persons who make these gestures may see themselves as guerrillas who have the mandate of the people to engage the common enemy, the Establishment. But of course they have no such mandate. A good many Americans may ardently desire radical social change, but only the smallest fraction thinks it reasonable to try to bring it about by means of irregular warfare. In this, and in the stockpiling of weapons in preparation for *der Tag*, the proponents of violence show a kind of holy simplicity. How do armed risings actually come about in industrialized countries? Almost uniformly, they begin with demonstrations and riots—often spontaneous in character. Then the demonstrators and rioters arm themselves from the public arsenals. This process, often repeated since the French Revolution, explains how the disarmed populations of Europe have managed time and again to turn up at the decisive moment with weapons in their hands. The method is efficient, it is cheap, and it is well known. What, then, is the purpose—even from the viewpoint of those who favor armed struggle—of privately acquiring assorted weapons of dubious military value in the expectation of someday putting them to use? In practice, arms caches of that kind are mere liabilities, exposing their possessors to legal sanctions—not to mention danger to life and limb. The reason that anyone bothers with such things has to be sought in the psychological disposition of the dissidents. Firstly, acquiring and hiding weapons is itself a form of symbolic activity that looks businesslike. Then, those radicals who identify themselves with the guerrilla forces of far-off countries are quite naturally led to imitate the policy of do-it-yourself in the matter of armaments, a program that makes military sense for the guerrillas but none at all under our own very different circumstances. Lastly, the possession of weapons may give some emotional satisfaction to people who are exposed to routine violence on the part of the police; that is the reason for the Black Panthers' open espousal of weapons for self-defense. Unfortunately, the weapons can give them no physical security.

The attention given in the Movement press to guerrilla activity abroad and imitations of it in this country helps explain a further curious displacement in the minds of our domestic militants. They sometimes talk and act as if they were the fighting arm of a population oppressed by a foreign power, one that maintains precarious bases among us, supported with difficulty by means of long supply-lines stretching to the other side of the world. In strategic terms, they imagine that they are in the position of Vietnamese or Latin-American guerrillas, and that American power is far away. But in fact the state is right here. Up to this point it has coped handily enough with the dissidents simply by managing the news, for a propaganda campaign is all that has been required to justify, to most people's satisfaction, the murder or imprisonment of the Black Panther leaders—extending to very minor leaders; the capacity of the Black Panthers to rock the boat has always been negligible, but their vulnerability and their usefulness to the government as scapegoats has been immense. The white radicals have thus far escaped the serious attentions of the state literally because of protective coloration. When the government is ready to suppress them, it will not have to mount an expeditionary force, it will pick up the telephone. And the inflammatory rhetoric of the radicals, the infantile talk about picking up the gun, will be a tailor-made excuse. For the state is very different from what they imagine it to be. It is the formal expression of the life of an entire society, representing the interests that have the greatest weight in determining the character and contours of that life—and its monopoly of the means of organized violence is assented to by the great majority of the population. There are indeed means by which such a state might be dismantled, but under the present conditions, armed insurrection is absolutely the least feasible expedient imaginable.

III

ONCE WE STOP thinking of making war against a state that is organized for that specific purpose, and has only to feel sufficiently threatened to employ its very nearly absolute power, it is possible to raise the discussion of social reform to a higher level. When we give up our preoccupation with infantry tactics, we free ourselves of certain ancillary delusions that otherwise tend to reduce a radical to a kind of two-bit General Patton without portfolio. It is manlier to leave such things to the state and its agents of violence, since it is our ideal not to imitate but to liberate ourselves from that very atmosphere. Certain practical matters change at once when we do so. Cop-baiting suddenly comes to look like the thing it is, a sport engaged in chiefly by middle-class collegians at the expense of their social inferiors—with a special kick to it because the policeman is both armed and under a restraining discipline; in the South, where the police are a good deal more ruthless, it is not fashionable to provoke or assault them. Our society is not very tender with human beings—every person in it is a victim—but the policeman represents a special degree of victimization. He is usually recruited from an economic and cultural level of the population that is near the bottom. In the city neighborhoods in which I was raised, boys grew up to join the force or go to jail, almost indifferently, and I knew families that were represented in both those institutions. The policeman is inducted into a special caste. His training and indoctrination are directed to a single object: making the country safe for the system of property relations favored by the powerful. The deformation of character he suffers may be greater or less than that of the other born losers he is paid to keep in line, but I imagine it must be substantial. In any case, the worker whose tools are club and pistol is a living reproach to the society that has bred and debauched him. What do we mean to do with the police on the morning after the revolution? Shoot them? Give their weapons and uniforms to a couple of hundred thousand new victims? Simply keep them on, but point out to them other groups than the poor as the proper object of their attentions? Clearly, a revolution no more original than that in its conception of decent social relations is not worth struggling for.

The matter is important, firstly, for our self-respect. Then it is important because the policeman is the usual point of contact between the dissenters and the state—as the army will be too if the situation warms up sufficiently. Considered simply as a question of tactics, it might be harmless to vilify the police and the army if they were disarmed and disorganized; that would be mere bigotry and class distaste, merely unrevolutionary. But as things are, we have a powerful motive for remembering that they are brothers of ours—members of the class whose labor pays for this discussion of politics and has bought the education of the persons taking part in it—and that their neutrality is the least condition for a successful revolution.

WHAT IS THE REAL vulnerability of this seeming monolith, the industrial state? To begin with, since like every other state its power is in the last analysis psychological, it suffers from all those pressures and forces that contribute to disaffection on the part of the citizens. In preindustrial societies, the psychological hold of governments upon their subject populations is relatively stable, because governments are always the expression of the relation of effective forces, and those forces themselves change but slowly in cultures that do not have the machine: ideology, religion, mores, means of production—all these are more or less fixed, and the state is proportionally secure. Highly industrialized societies, on the other hand, are by definition evolving rapidly. It is of their essence to be eclectic and heterodox in their public philosophy and presuppositions, and they are proportionately unstable, most especially since a modern economy generates strains and discontents on the same scale as its material productivity.

This is very nearly as true of the Soviet Union as it is of the United States. Such polities, whatever their formal structure, depend upon consent in a manner unthinkable before the modern era; precisely because they are undergoing rapid change in the normal course of their evolution, the question of their legitimacy is always being raised anew, and larger and larger sections of the population have to be bribed or cozened into giving their consent. No longer than a decade ago it was widely assumed by social scientists that the modern state, with its enormous industrial resources and its control of the media of information, could always allay psychological strains by according a larger share of privilege and amenity to those who cried the loudest at any given time. The assumption was enshrined in various formulas, optimistic (Daniel Bell: the end of ideology) or pessimistic (Herbert Marcuse: one-dimensional man). But the human cuss has proved to be too much for these prophets. He has lusts that they overlooked and that cannot be gratified by this system, for all its wealth. There are privileges and amenities that the capitalist and socialist factories do not produce—for example, creative work, the soul's necessary aliment, and its further expression in a politics whose order is not violence but equity. So the college students, the spoiled darlings of the richest nations in the world, erupted here and in Europe. It is extremely doubtful that their fever has been permanently allayed.

As an index of how ticklish a matter it is to elicit the consent of the governed under present-day conditions, consider President Nixon's chances for reelection as these words are being written. Prices are high, unemployment is high, the stock market is rising at last but still shaky—and these relatively mild disturbances make it unlikely that Mr. Nixon can succeed himself in office and give the Republican Party an additional four years in which to control the wealth of the nation. That is, unless he does something dramatic that will distract men's minds. At this writing, he appears to be expanding the theater of war to include Laos. Now, an expanded war conducted with diminishing forces is a curious strategy. It may not be the whole of his strategy—the North Vietnamese, at least, appear to believe that it is not, for in the week in which this is written, C. L. Sulzberger reported from Paris that the North Vietnamese have been inquiring anxiously of their foreign contacts there about the likelihood of President Nixon's employing tactical atomic weapons in the war. Mr. Sulzberger himself regards the possibility as unlikely, because of the domestic repercussions to be anticipated. I hope he is right, but the military logic of the situation points in that direction. Conventional air-power has been expended liberally in Vietnam without effecting its purpose, and the pressure to use the ultimate weapon is therefore very strong. Given the temper of this Administration, unrest within the United States as a result of the government's use of atomic weapons might very well appeal to our leaders as providing an opportunity for settling once and for all with the dissenters. Here is a conceivable course of action for the government: A demonstration in force near the border of North Vietnam, or an actual incursion into it, designed to provoke a large concentration of North Vietnamese troops, against whom tactical atomic weapons could be employed. General Giap is unlikely to respond in that way to a foray that remains a mere demonstration—his strategy is hostile to pitched battles except under the most favorable circumstances—so that the American generals may plan for, or be led into, attempts to intensify the situation. At that point, there are many possibilities for doing so, but the probable outcome is, at one moment or another, the use of atomic weapons against the city of Hanoi. Once those weapons had been employed, the President could announce that this course of action had been dictated by the desire to save American lives in a moment of great peril, declare war or not, as he chose, and mobilize the armed forces completely.

That is the kind of contingency that can crystallize the revolutionary process that we are living through at this moment. That, or some move similarly inspired, appears to me to be not merely conceivable but reasonably likely before the end of the current Presidential term. Foreign pressures, internal unrest arising from economic troubles and the disgust aroused by the unresolved war, as well as the character of Mr. Nixon, make some such coup seem probable. Or it might take the form of military intervention in the next Latin-American country to expropriate American holdings, for the danger of fighting two wars at once may be outweighed, in the judgment of the Administration, by the danger of the deteriorating domestic situation, which the Republicans thus far have managed only to intensify. For a Left that is prepared to put into practice the principles of nonviolent revolution, such an eventuality may offer a very short period in which to do so.

IV

To ACT ALWAYS in the spirit of that polity we hope to see established. What is that polity—what is politics, first of all? We have heard the usual definitions: *Who gets what and how much. The art of the possible. War by other means. A racket.* These cynicisms can certainly be applied to this or that aspect of the politics that we are being treated to, but they do not exhaust the subject. Rightly understood, politics is the sum of men's public and private activities; it comprehends the life of a social being. To regard those activities as falling of necessity under the sign of one or another form of organized disregard for men's talents, needs, preferences, and aspirations is to reason too exclusively from the practice of the venal, violent societies it is our aim to replace. That most men should reason so is understandable; properly speaking, they do not reason on the question at all, but adopt formulas designed at once to express their frustration and relieve them of responsibility for it. But for persons calling themselves revolutionaries to think essentially in the same terms amounts to a confession of incapacity. And yet that is the commonest case. Old Left and New Left believe at bottom that their business is to dispatch their adversaries and then proceed to give laws to a grateful populace. It is not clear that their performance in that respect would improve much on that of our present rulers. In any case, the society that answers to our desire is one in which there are no adversaries to be chastened by a generations-long campaign of hectoring, imprisonment, and murder, and therefore it would be absurd for us to set about building it by such means of violence as might be at our command. All former states have depended upon coercive sanctions, and the ultimate sanction has always been murder. But we are not interested in another state of that kind. Indeed, if we are consistent, in planning for a manlike polity we are not interested in a state at all.

Men have to secure the means of life. All government is a more or less heavy tax upon the necessary activity for securing the means of life, and a diverting of the energies of the greatest number to the service of the few. It has been tolerated thus far for various more or less adequate reasons. But at the present time, the chief excuse for keeping up the practice is the superstition that government is synonymous with organization and ordered effort. Industrial society clearly requires a great deal of organizing: ergo, government. Preindustrial society also required a great deal of organizing, apparently, for it too was amply governmented. And while in practice ninety-nine percent of men's activities are organized without benefit of government, in despite of government, in violation of government's express ordinances, the popular theory has it that such a state of affairs could not possibly maintain itself, for that would amount to chaos—or anarchy, the terms being understood as equivalent. When pushed to the wall, the defenders of government argue that at very least the state provides the formal framework within which men organize their activities, and its institutions facilitate their doing so, if only by establishing traffic rules. That is true in this sense, that the state, the executive organ of the class that holds effective power, regulates the traffic by means of which we draw our rations and are mulcted of the product of our labor; it is the guarantor of the money-system—that is, the system of accounting by which our masters can reckon and regulate how much we cost them and how much they make on the deal; and it intimidates or punishes those who jib at taking part in this process, or those who have nothing to contribute to it. For the masters, a government is clearly essential. For the rest of us, a government is simply the most generalized instrument of our subjection. Above all, it provides that our intercourse with one another will be regulated by force.

Not useless so much as actively pernicious to men who aspire to live their own lives, this formidable state is nevertheless a shaky affair, and now more so than ever before in history. As the national economy has grown to be coextensive with the entire population, and no one man can withdraw completely from the market whether as producer or consumer, since to do so would be to starve, the government must attempt to regulate more persons more absolutely than at any time in the past. That is what the information banks are all about. Moreover, the entire mechanism of production and distribution which was, a hundred years ago, divided into thousands of discrete units, is now a single organism, and a perturbation anywhere within it disrupts and disorganizes the whole. The matter stands thus: although the greatest number of the citizens very properly shrink from initiating violence as a solution to their troubles, and are likely to be out of sympathy with those who suggest it, that does not mean that they cannot be persuaded to adopt means of relief less dangerous and less repugnant to decency. (It must be remembered that to most men at most times the violence of the state seems decent because it is customary, and because it masquerades as the guarantor of order.) Such means are ready to hand —they have developed together with the progressive emancipation of the work-force to its present condition of mitigated wage-slavery. Essentially they are three: the vote, the boycott, and the strike.

THE FIRST OF THESE is the weakest, as it must be under a system in which the rulers frame the issues to be arbitrated, and regard a popular vote as, at best, advisory. Two presidents have been elected to office on their promises to end the war in Vietnam. The next one may well achieve office on the same promise, to turn in the same performance. And while the majority of the people may contemn the war, the majority of Congress need not—witness the fate of the Hatfield-McGovern bill. The vote, then, is likely to be effective only in connection with side-issues, and the prospect for dismantling the coercive machinery of government by balloting is as slim as the method is indirect. Nevertheless it has a function in the struggle for a decent society, and that is to make it as difficult as possible for the government to go about its business of oppressing us. Let us take the case of a candidate for political office who pledges himself to work for peace. If he is a candidate for the Presidency, that pledge will not help us in deciding whether or not to vote for him, since his opponent will say the same thing—we have reached a point where anyone who aspires to that post must make that lying concession to the public temper. If the peace candidate presents himself for some lesser office, he may very well have an opponent who supports the Administration's foreign policy, which means that he will offer no resistance to the war's indefinite prolongation. What if the peace candidate gets our vote, wins, and works—say, in the Congress—for peace? Well, if the war lasts long enough, he may some day find himself in the majority, and vote us out of the war. But until that possibly far-distant time, our vote will have done next to nothing to stop the war. That suggests that the

more significant policy would be to use the ballot negatively even in such a case; obvious abstentions and small
turnouts generally are seriously embarrassing to political
parties, whose *ultima ratio* is: We may not be much, but
the People want us in office. In this connection, we should
remember that both of our political parties are responsible
for the war, that it could not go on ten minutes more without the cooperation of either. Now, abstention has to make
itself visible. It won't do to simply stay away from the
polls. An active don't-vote campaign—particularly on an
issue connected with the war, where it is plain that what
the country wants it will not get—seems to me to be highly
eligible.

As for an economic boycott, when such a thing is practicable at all, that is, when a significant number of con-
sumers can be persuaded to keep their money in their jeans,
it is a kind of absolute weapon, since it is almost impossible
to retaliate against. In most cases it is also impossible to
identify the persons employing it, but that is an advantage
that must be sacrificed, because in a struggle of this kind
it is essential to let people know what the object is and
who thinks so. A boycott threatens to interfere with the
livelihood of everyone connected with the manufacture and
distribution of the commodity that is singled out for neglect. In so serious a matter, it is obviously important that
the persons refusing to buy take responsibility openly for
their action. For Americans the automobile is a necessity,
but it is not essential that every car-owner have a new one
at the customary rhythm of replacement. If the trade were
reduced in a short time by perhaps ten percent, that drop
might very well precipitate a general economic depression.
Indeed the mere rumor of a concerted attempt of this kind
could have serious effects. Only the weightiest reasons can
justify the use of such a weapon, which punishes the innocent. In this case, the reasons appear to me to be weighty
as could be imagined—that our first order of business is to
stop murdering the Vietnamese. Given the fact that the
American people has no desire to exterminate the people
of Vietnam, and has only been persuaded to do so thus far
by systematic lying about all the issues involved, I should
judge that the disruption of the American economy by

boycott would be a small price to pay for ending that in-
famy. I have resolved not to buy a new car—or a used one
—as long as the war lasts, and I invite those of my readers
who are like-minded to do the same and say so publicly.
To those persons who have organizing talents, I suggest
that they consider going beyond the personal gesture and
setting on foot a boycott campaign directed against the
automobile. It would be more effective than many mass
demonstrations, far more likely to persuade the government
to stop doing murder in our name.

FINALLY, THERE IS the tactic of the strike, or more especially what has been called the general strike. The idea
has had a long, confused history, and till quite recently
had lost credit as an instrument of political action. When
it was first elaborated by European anarcho-syndicalists in
the 1880's, it was a reflection of the beginnings of effective
labor organization. The anarcho-syndicalists chose the industrial strike as the appropriate instrument for bringing
about social change in an industrial environment as earlier
anarchists, in a less industrialized era, had favored armed
insurrection. In the same way, for these theorists the labor
union was the strategic social unit that the commune had
been for their predecessors. However, the economies of
the nations of Western Europe were still far from being
fully industrialized at that period; besides the fact that
the largest number of workers was still employed in agri-
culture, manufacturing itself was characterized by many
small units, each producing on a relatively small scale and
employing relatively few workers. Under these circumstances, unionization, too, was limited in extent, and individual unions were limited in power. Accordingly, the idea
of a concerted strike on the part of a labor force whose
work was essential to the functioning of the industrial
machine as a whole, came into being somewhat before its
time.

During the next three decades, industrialization and
unionization grew rapidly in Europe and America, and the
theory of the general strike became proportionately per-
suasive. Nevertheless, with the coming of the First World
War, two influences combined to undermine this tactic as

a political weapon. First, a basic assumption of the theory was the international solidarity of the organized workers, for it was obvious that a revolution in any one country brought about by a general strike would be threatened with suppression by invasion—for capital, at least, was international in its organization—and this protective reaction could only be defeated in turn by the solidarity of foreign workers who would paralyze the war machines of their respective countries by general strikes of their own. The First World War, and the spectacle of the socialist deputies in the Reichstag voting war credits for the Kaiser, breached workers' solidarity so effectively as to destroy the legend permanently, and in the process severely damage the theoretical practicability of the general strike. Then, in 1917 the Russian Revolution broke out, and it exerted thereafter an enormous attraction, leading among other things to what was understood to be the Leninist model of revolution in general, emphasizing the role of the vanguard party and the necessity for an armed uprising. Another result of the success of the Russian Revolution was the general discrediting of the anarchist movement (until 1917, industrial unionism and unionism of any kind on the Continent was heavily anarchist in doctrine and personnel) on the part of the Left, and the condemnation of policies associated with it.

In other words, the theory of the general strike was a casualty of history: its validity appeared to have been contradicted by the evolution of society itself, while in fact the tests had been less than conclusive. Since 1917, of course, unionization has grown to be almost coextensive with industry, so that labor unions are an important feature of mature capitalist society. This means that the potential political power of the industrial working class has also increased, and in theory that power might be exercised in a general strike. Further, another class of workers has developed in numbers and power since the beginning of the century in a manner that could scarcely have been foreseen. Most of these workers belong to what we call the middle class in this country, assorted professionals, technicians, clerks, who are relatively favored in status and income, but who still fulfill Marx's definition of the proletarian: the man who must sell his labor in order to live. The status of this group is at present insecure, and so is its psychology. In general, it is subject to severe economic and emotional strains, just as much as the other strata in industrial societies. And its position in the machinery of production and distribution is strategic. In short, the appropriate conditions for employing the political weapon of the general strike, first envisioned a century ago, have at last been realized.

In theory, a general strike means the complete cessation of productive work on the part of the entire work-force. The suggestion may not be as difficult to achieve as it appears at first sight; stoppages in strategic sectors only might conceivably affect the entire industrial machine by creating shortages of goods and services at points in the productive process remote from the original loci of disruption. Now, the idea of the general strike flourished particularly in France before the First World War, when the economic system was not yet as highly integrated as it is today. In other words, pre-1914 France was a relatively ill-adapted proving-ground for the theory. But by 1968 the system of production and distribution had evolved to the point where a strike of ten million workers was found practicable, and the strike effectively paralyzed economic life in France. The May days fell short of successful revolution, but they brought about the fall of the De Gaulle government. The future may show that the most important consequence of the entire episode was its demonstration of the feasibility of the general strike.

THE STRIKE WAS BEGUN by the students, over political and ideological issues that one might have imagined held little interest for the country's industrial workers—who had been treated to a rising standard of living in recent years, like those of our own country, though they were not yet at the relative income-level of the American workers. The student demonstrations were opposed by the police, with a good deal of violence. A surprise: residents of the Latin Quarter in Paris, the scene of the worst of the fighting, generally showed sympathy for the students. At this point the young people sent delegates to the factories, asking for support from the workers. In factory after factory, the workers gave a political interpretation to their own grievances, and the strike became general. At its height, the technical and professional personnel of the television industry—a government monopoly in France—decided that their own grievances as employees, and the censorship they were subjected to in trying to report the tumultuous happenings in France, were reason enough to join the strike. How De Gaulle and the French Communist Party managed to keep the strike from developing into a revolution has been described a number of times by competent analysts—and notably by Daniel Singer in his excellent recent book, *Prelude to Revolution: France in May of 1968.*

For our purposes, the lesson of May 1968 is that the fabric of industrial society is now so closely knit, and all elements of the population have such cause to be dissatisfied with the tenor of their lives, that a refusal to go along as usual in any one sector can probably find effectual echoes in all the others. When, as a result of the invasion of Cambodia last year, and the shooting of students at Jackson and Kent State, there were widespread student strikes, workers in the book-publishing industry in New York—encouraged by the fact that a conference of their employers had passed resolutions condemning the war—voted to consider a general strike. As it happened, no such action was decided upon, but the significant thing is that it was considered. If the government had not already given hasty promises to withdraw from Cambodia, a radical measure of that kind might well have been adopted in the publishing trade—an industry that has never known a union—as it was adopted by the portion of the film industry established in New York. In other words, the public resentment aroused by the invasion and the shootings was not so high that it could not be placated by equivocal government pledges and the hope held out by the hastily introduced Hatfield-McGovern bill. The next such occasion may well be more serious, and it would be useful to be psychologically prepared at that time to render the vote of no confidence that the government has been courting.

IT WOULD BE PUERILE, however, to imagine that the most

effective use of the vote, the boycott, and the general strike could act upon the government so as to permanently correct its tendency to bully its own citizens and slaughter foreigners. These are essential characteristics of government in general—grown intolerable in the twentieth century because of the destructive power of modern armaments. The only way to reform the government is to dissolve it. Therefore, the aim of the nonviolent measures we are discussing can scarcely be to have a Democratic administration succeed the present Republican one in the shortest period contemplated by the law. Rather, since the members of those clubs can show no record of social service to balance the tax of life that they exact from the rest of us, our object should be to see to it that they are permanently cashiered. And to persuade the largest number that an absence of government is no negative achievement, we should begin to sketch our idea of how the American people might choose to conduct their affairs once they had the managing of them in their own hands. The best way to do so is to frame a program so obviously wholesome and desirable that the persons we wish to influence will be led first to approve of it in the abstract, and then to wonder why so worthy a list of projects is unthinkable under the existing system. To try to draw here a detailed portrait of the benevolent anarchist polity of the future would be foolish, for that is clearly the work of the future. But there are some ideals that are, emotionally and morally speaking, near at hand, and, under our current social arrangements, impossible of attainment. Here are some that come to mind.

Complete disarmament, and disbanding of all armed forces. Modern weapons are simply instruments of mass suicide. America had best drop the whole business, unilaterally. The money and effort saved can be put to use civilizing the nation.

Equality of status between men and women. This is to be promoted as the women see fit, in accordance with their interpretation of equality. Men are unfitted by their training to recognize the arbitrary disabilities imposed upon women by custom. As John Stuart Mill remarked pertinently a hundred years ago, talent is not so cheap that we can afford to sacrifice the abilities of half the human race.

Besides, slavery is an unhappy arrangement for slaves and slaveholders alike.

Equality of status among all persons. There is no point in proposing that women enjoy equality with a sex nine-tenths of which is in industrial servitude. For that reason, every citizen must have an equal share of whatever civility we have attained to—equal income, equal education, equal access to useful work. A corollary is control by all workers of the enterprises they work in.

Money restricted to nontransferable claims upon the public stock of necessities and amenities. The monetization of our values is now absolute, and we have found out by experiment that this condition amounts to a disease of the soul. Under the present system, money is necessarily invidious power. Since we do not care to perpetuate relations of power among men, we must disestablish money along with government, reducing it to a scrip available to everyone in equal measure, for subsistence and luxury.

It will be seen that these proposals are not such as require to be imposed by force. Very few people are so sincerely set upon blowing up the world that they would be grieved if the means of doing so were unavailable. The great majority of men and women would prefer honest equality to demeaning privilege if our mores permitted them to choose. The money question has become so otiose that we can no longer persuade our young people to take a seemly interest in it. So these are examples of nonviolent social arrangements, all of them radical and revolutionary enough to be worth the bother. More will readily suggest themselves, but these will do for openers.

The Board Meeting

Lennart Bruce

WE sit and doodle
when somebody utters
a series of sounds

I close my eyes
one eyeball gets stuck
I roll the other one,

tearing it loose from its lid
the muscle I use
is the most tenacious of my body.

My voice is let loose
the graph of its sound rises & sinks
with my personality-flow.

Some members start nodding at me,
nodding back I feel tears of joy rising
my mouth closes over the resonance

of a fading sound.
I finish by waving my left hand
quick like the wing of a bird.

Somebody on my right does likewise
but for the opposite reason
I feel animosity surging. The chairman

declares the meeting adjourned. We rise
I have a feeling of gratefulness
mixed with hysteria. We're all smiling now.

Automatically I seize

my penis through my pocket
I see everybody does it

and my hand flies up.
We bow formally; something
moves in me,

through me,
a feeling the meeting
went my way.

Good News From Section D

Rick DeMarinis

Sunday again and the rain has made
oatmeal of the first three sections
of the Los Angeles Times. The usual
front-page disasters are melting
into each other. The saddened secretary
of health is sliding across
the amputated hand of the president.
Contracts with space are being cancelled
faster than the highway patrol can count
bodies.
            Where are we going?
asks a spiritual leader of the U.S.
Weather Bureau. I dump the gray mess
and turn to the first dry section,
section D. It's the sports section
and the first good news in weeks.

Peru, in spite of quakes
and long-distance looting
went on a scoring spree, clinching
a berth in the quarterfinals.
      Someone who bet a bundle
at Belmont is sitting pretty, six to one.

      Sitting pretty in the kitchen
with the other dry section
my wife is six months' pregnant
with more good news. My heart
is misfiring steadily with its fifth cup
of Taster's Choice and my eyes are keyed
with bulletins:
      Soccer fans in Zambia
have charged the officials with witchcraft!
Deep in this copper-rich country
there are athletes who become crocodiles
at will!
      The novice in his amniotic sea
is swimming through time.
It's a distance swim toward light
and the mystery of the games.
The World Cup is at stake
and he is stroking the waters
      of his first woman.

Headlines from the next century
are brittle with age. The bishop
and weatherman are gone.
Section D is dry to the bone
with pure announcement:
      It's the season's opener
and the game starts at one

      rain or shine.

A Course in Film-Making

Norman Mailer

I: ON THE THEORY

THE COMPANY, jaded and exhausted, happily or unhappily sexed-out after five days and nights of moviemaking
and balling in midnight beds and pools, had been converted
to a bunch of enforced existentialists by the making of the
film. There is no other philosophical word which will apply
to the condition of being an actor who has never acted
before, finding himself in a strange place with a thorough-
going swap of strangers and familiars for bedfellows, no
script, and a story which suggests that the leading man is a
fit and appropriate target for assassination. Since many of
the actors were not without their freaks, their kinks, or
old clarion calls to violence, and since the word of the
Collective Rumor was that more than one of the men was
packing a piece, a real piece with bullets, these five days
and nights had been the advanced course in existentialism.
Nobody knew what was going to happen, but for one
hundred and twenty hours the conviction had been growing
that if the warning system of one's senses had been worth
anything in the past, something was most certainly going to
happen before the film was out. Indeed on several separate
occasions, it seemed nearly to happen. A dwarf almost
drowned in a pool, a fight had taken place, then a bad fight,
and on the night before at a climactic party two hours of
the most intense potential for violence had been filmed, yet
nothing commensurate had happened. The company was
now in that state of hangover, breath foul with swallowed
curses and congestions of the instincts, which comes to

prizefight fans when a big night, long awaited, ends as a lackluster and lumbering waltz. Not that the party had been a failure while it was being filmed. The tension of the party was memorable in the experience of many. But, finally, nothing happened.

So, at this point next day in the filming of *Maidstone*, on the lazy afternoon which followed the night of the party, the director had come to the erroneous conclusion his movie was done—even though the film was still continuing in the collective mind of some working photographers before whom the director was yet to get hit on the head by a hammer wielded by his best actor, and would respond by biting the best actor on the ear, a fight to give him a whole new conception of his movie. What a pity to remind ourselves of these violent facts, for they encourage interest in a narrative which will not be presented in a hurry and then only a little, and that after an inquiry into the director's real interest which is (less bloody and more philosophical) the possible real nature of film—not an easy discussion since the director has already found a most special way of making movies. When he begins to discourse on the subject, he feels as if he is not so much a director as an Argument. He can literally think of himself as The Argument, some medieval wind—a Player who is there for harangue. Certainly in that precise hour of the afternoon when he took off his actor's cape and moved from Norman T. Kingsley back to Norman Mailer again, and gave an orientation on the grass of Gardiner's Island, it could hardly be said that he failed to talk about his movie to the company. No, he made every effort, even went so far as to explain that his way of making films was analogous to a military operation, to a commando raid on the nature of reality—they would discover where reality was located by the attack itself, just as a company of Rangers might learn that the enemy was located not in the first town they invaded but another. Of course, even as he spoke, he felt the resumption of tension. There was still something wrong in the air. The picture, he could swear, but for some fill-in, was finished, yet the presence it created had not left.

He could, however, hardly complain if the film itself was still a *presence*. A condition of dread had been generated over the last five days which had put subtle terror and tension into the faces of people who had never acted before, lines of such delicate intent and fine signification as to draw the envy of professionals. That had been precisely the presence he wished to elicit. It was the fundament of his method, the heart of his confidence, to put untried actors into situations without a script and film them with simple or available lighting, work in the limitations of these means and unforeseen ends and exits to get the best available sound (which was not always near to superb), and yet, all limitations granted, he could by this method give a sense of the bewildering surface of his cinematic reality which was finer by far than the work of all but the very best film artists.

It was in other words, a Leviathan of a thesis, and he, with characteristic modesty, ignorant until a few years ago of nearly all to do with film-making, and still technically more ignorant than the good majority of mediocre directors, was still convinced he had wandered by easy progressions into a most complex and devilish way of working up a film. And now had the confidence he was a film-maker. And the unique experience to convince himself that he was a pioneer, for he believed he had come upon a way to smash the machine which crushed every surface of cinematic reality, that organization of plot, dialogue, sets, professionals, schedules, and thundering union impedimenta which beat every effort to take a good story or a book and flesh it into movie film. No, something was wrong with that, something was dreadfully wrong with a process which wasted time, talent, and millions of dollars at a crack to produce cinematic works of the most predictable encapsulation. One could sit through such works and on rare occasion even enjoy a world of good taste and nice insight without ever a moment of sensuous discomfort, which was exactly equal to saying without a moment of aesthetic revelation.

Still it is something to skip at a leap over thirty years of movie-making apprenticeship he has not served, to propose that, all ignorance and limitations granted, he has found a novel technique, and is on the consequence ready to issue a claim that his way of putting a film together, cut by cut, is important, and conceivably closer to the nature of film than the work of other, more talented directors.

2.

OF COURSE, he makes no second claim that technically, gymnastically, pyrotechnically, or by any complex measure of craft does he begin to know the secrets of the more virtuoso of the directors and the cutters, no, he would only say that the material he has filmed lends itself happily, even innocently, to whole new ways of making cuts. That is because it has captured the life it was supposed to photograph. He is unfolding no blueprint. So there tends to be less monotony to his composition, less of a necessity to have overillumined and too simplified frames, less of a push to give a single emphasis to each scene. His lines of dramatic force are not always converging toward the same point—nobody in his frame has yet learned to look for the reaction of the hero after the villain insults him, no, his film is not diminished by supporting actors who are forever obliged to indicate what the point of the scene is supposed to be (and are thereby reminiscent of dutiful relatives at a family dinner). So, his movie is not reminiscent of other films where the scene, no matter how superb, has a hollow —not so pervasive perhaps as the cheerful hollow in the voices of visitors who have come to be cheerful to a patient in a hospital, but there, even in the best of films always there. In the worst of films it is like the cordiality at the reception desk in a mortician's manor. So it could even be said that professional movie acting consists of the ability to reduce the hollow to an all but invisible hole, and one can measure such actors by their ability to transcend the hollow. Marlon Brando could go "Wow" in *Waterfront* and Dustin Hoffman would limp to the kitchen sink in *Midnight*

Cowboy and the lack of life in the conventional movie frame was replaced by magical life. One could speak with justice of great actors. Perhaps a thousand actors and two thousand films can be cited where the movie frame comes alive and there is no dip at the foot of consciousness because something is false at the root.

Nonetheless any such appearance of talent was close to magic. The conventional way of making most films usually guaranteed its absence. For there was an element which interfered with motion pictures as much as the blurring of print would hinder the reading of a book, and this flaw derived from the peculiar misapprehension with which the silent film gave way to sound, the supposition that sound-and-film was but an extension of the theater, even as the theater was but an extension of literature. It was assumed that movies were there to tell a story. The story might derive from the stage, or from the pages of a book, or even from an idea for a story, but the film was asked to issue from a detailed plan which would have lines of dialogue. The making of the movie would be a fulfillment of that script, that literary plan; so, each scene would be shaped like a construction unit to build the architecture of the story. It was one of those profoundly false assumptions which seem at the time absolute common sense, yet it was no more natural than to have insisted that a movie was a river and one should always experience, while watching a film, emotions analogous to an afternoon spent on the banks of a stream. That might have been seen instantly as confining, a most confining notion; but to consider the carryover of the story from literature to the film as equally constricting—no, that was not very evident.

For few people wished to contemplate the size of the job in transporting a novelist's vision of life over to a film; indeed, who in the movie business was going to admit that once literary characters had been converted over to actors, they could not possibly produce the same relation to other actors that the characters once had to each other? Interpretations had to collide. If each actor had his own idea of the dialogue he committed to memory, be certain the director had a better idea. And the producer! Lifetimes of professional craft go into halving such conceptual differences. The director gives up a little of his interpretation, then a little more, then almost all of it. The actor is directed away from his favorite misconceptions (and conceptions). Both parties suffer the rigor mortis of the technical conditions—which are not so close to a brightly lit operating theater as to a brightly lit morgue. Then the scriptwriter has dependably delivered the scenario with his own private —and sometimes willful—idea buried in it (and if the work is an adaptation, odd lines of the novelist are still turning over). The coherence of the original novel has been cremated and strewn. Now the film is being made with conflicting notions of those scattered ashes. Of course the director is forced back willy-nilly to his script. It is all he can finally depend upon. Given the fundamental, nay, even organic, confusion on a movie set over what everybody is really doing, the company has to pool all differences and be faithful to the script even when the script has lost any relation to the original conception, and has probably begun to constrict the real life which is beginning to emerge on the set. No wonder great novels invariably make the most disappointing movies, and modest novels (like *The Asphalt Jungle*) sometimes make very good movies. It is because the original conception in modest novels is less special and so more capable of being worked upon by any number of other writers, directors, and actors.

Still, the discussion has been too narrow. The film after all, is fed not only by literature but by the theater, and the theater is a conspicuous example of how attractively a blueprint can be unfolded. In fact, the theater is reduced to very little whenever the collaboration between actors and script is not excellent. Yet the theater has had to put up with many a similar difficulty. Can it be said that something works in the theater which only pretends to work in the film? If the first error perpetrated upon movies has been to see them as an adjunct of literature, perhaps the second is the rush to make film an auxiliary of the theatrical arts, until even movies considered classics are hardly more than pieces of filmed theater.

Of course a film lover could counter by saying that he

was not necessarily thinking only of such monuments as *Gone With the Wind* when he used the term classic. In fact, he would inquire about *A Night at the Opera* or *The Maltese Falcon*.

The difficulties had obviously begun. The Argument would be never so simple again. The Marx Brothers, for example, stampeded over every line of a script and tore off in enough directions to leave concepts fluttering like ticker tape on the mysterious nature of the movie art. Certainly, any attempt to declare *The Maltese Falcon* a piece of filmed theater would have to confess that *The Maltese Falcon* was more, a mysterious ineffable possession of "more" and that was precisely what one looked for in a film. It was a hint to indicate some answer to the secrets of film might begin to be found in the curious and never quite explained phenomenon of the movie star. For Humphrey Bogart was certainly an element of natural film, yes, even *the* element which made *The Maltese Falcon* more than an excellent piece of filmed theater. Thinking of the evocative aesthetic mists of that movie, how could the question not present itself: why did every piece of good dramatic theater have to be the enemy of the film? It was unhappily evident to The Argument that any quick and invigorating theses on the character of movie stars and the hidden nature of the movie might have to wait for a little exposition on the special qualities of theater.

3.

A COMPLEX matter. You might, for instance, have to take into account why people who think it comfortable to be nicely drunk at the beginning of a play would find it no pleasure to go to a movie in the same condition. Pot was more congenial for a film. If the difference for most hard-working actors between movies and theater seemed hardly more than a trip across a crack, the split to any philosopher of the film was an abyss, just that same existential abyss which lies between booze and the beginnings of the psychedelic.

Existentially, theater and film were in different dominions (and literature was probably nearer to each of them than they were to each other). The theater was a ceremony with live priests who had learned by rote to pool their aesthetic instincts for a larger purpose. So theater partook of a near-obscene ceremony: it imitated life in a living place, and it had real people as the imitators. Such imitation was either sacrilege to the roots of life, or a reinforcement of them. Certainly, sentiments called religious appeared ready to arise whenever a group of people attended a ceremony in a large and dimly lit place. But in fact anyone who has ever experienced a moment of unmistakable balance between the audience, the cast, the theater and the *manifest* of the play, an awe usually remarked by a silence palpable as the theatrical velvet of an unvoiced echo, knows that the foundation of the theater is in the church and in the power of kings, or at least knows, if theater goes back to blood sacrifices performed in a cave—which is about where the most advanced theater seems ready to go—that the more recent foundations were ecclesiastical and royal. Theater, at all of its massive best, can be seen as equal to a ceremony, performed by noblemen who have power to chastise an audience, savage them, dignify them, warm them, marry their humors, even create a magical forest where each human on his seat is a tree and every sense is vibrating to the rustle of other leaves. One's roots return then to some lost majesty of pomp and power. Of course, theater is seldom so good. None of us have had a night like that recently. Still, theater has its minutes: a scene whose original concept was lost in the mixing of too many talents is recovered by the power of the actor to open relations with his audience. While he is engaged in an emotional transaction which is false by its nature (because he knows by heart the lines of apparently spontaneous passion he will say next), still he has to be true to the honest difficulty of not knowing whether the audience will believe him or not. His position onstage is existential—he cannot know in advance if his effort will succeed or not. In turn, the audience must respect him. For he is at the least brave enough to dare their displeasure. And if he is bad enough . . . well, how can he forget old nightmares where audiences kill actors? So the actor onstage is at once a fraud (because he pretends to emotion he cannot by any Method feel absolutely—*or he would be mad*) and yet is a true man engaged in a tricky venture, dangerous in its potentialities for humiliation. That is the strength of the theater. A vision of life somewhat different each night comes into existence between the actors and the audience, and what has been lost in the playwright's vision is sometimes transcended by the mood of a high theatrical hearth.

We are speaking of course only of the best and freshest plays. Even in a good play something dies about the time an actor recognizes that he can be mediocre in his performance and survive. The reputation of the play has become so useful that the audience has become a touch mediocre as well; at this point in the season the actor inevitably becomes as interesting as a whore in a house after her favorite client has gone for the night.

Nonetheless, it is still reminiscent of orgy to have relations with two worlds of sentience at once, and when fresh, theater is orgy. Onstage, the actor is in communion with the audience, and up to his neck in relations with other actors (if they are all still working together). A world of technique supports them. There are ways and means to live and act with half-thought-out lines of dialogue and errors of placement by the director, ways to deal with sentiments which have no ring and situations one knows by heart and still must enter with a pretense of theatrical surprise. An actor's culture exists, after all, for the working up of the false into the all-but-true; actors know the audience will carry the all-but-true over into the real and emotionally stirring if given a chance. So actors develop a full organ of emotional manifests. Large vibrant voices, significant moves. It all works because the actor is literally alive on a stage and therefore can never be false altogether. His presence is the real truth: he is at once the royal center of all eyes, and a Christian up before lions. So his theatrical emotion (which bears the same relation to real emotion which veneer of walnut bears to walnut) is moved by the risk of his position into a technique which offers truth. A

skillful actor with false gestures and false emotions elicits
our admiration because he tries to establish a vault under
which we can seize on the truth since, after all, he has told
the lie so well. Why, then, must that be an emotional transaction light-years of the psyche away from the same
transaction carried over to film?

4.

IT IS BECAUSE the risk in film is of other varieties. No audience is present unless the actor plays his scene for the cameramen and the union grips. And that is a specific audience
with the prejudices and tastes of policemen. Indeed they
usually dress like cops off-duty and are built like cops
(with the same heavy meat in the shoulders, same bellies
oiled on beer), which is not surprising for they are also in
surveillance upon a criminal activity: people are forging
emotions under bright lights.

But it is no longer false emotion brought by technique
to a point where it can be breathed upon and given life by
audiences who do not know the next line. No, now the
crew is a set of skills and intelligences. They are as sophisticated to the lines of the scene as the actors themselves.
Like cops they see through every fake move and hardly
care. The camera must move on cue and the sound boom,
the lights be shifted and the walls slid apart—the action
is easily as complex as a professional football team running
through the intricacies of a new play or preparing a defense against it.

In fact, the actor does not usually play for the technicians. It is the director whose intelligence he will feel first,
a charged critical intelligence knowing more of the scene
than himself, a center of authority altogether different from
a theatrical audience's authority (which is ready to relax
with every good sound the actor makes). The movie director, however, does not relax then. The good sound of the
actor can turn the plot inside out. No, here, the actor must
work into a focus of will. The real face he speaks to, whether
a step or ten steps to the side of the director, is a circle of

glass as empty of love as an empty glass. That lens is his final audience. It takes precedence over the director and even over the actors he plays with. In the moment of his profoundest passion, as he reaches forward to kiss the heroine with every tenderness, his lips to be famous for their quiver, he is of course slowly and proficiently bringing his mouth up to the erogenous zone of the lens.

Onstage, an actor, after twenty years of apprenticeship, can learn to reach the depths of an audience at the moment he is employing the maximum of his technique. A film actor with equivalent technique will have developed superb skills for revealing his reaction to the circle of glass. He can fail every other way, disobey the director or appear incapable of reacting to his direction, leave the other actors isolated from him and with nothing to react to, he can even get his lines wrong, but if he has film technique he will look sensational in the rushes, he will bring life to the scene even if he was death on the set. It is not surprising. There is something sinister about film. *Film is a phenomenon whose resemblance to death has been ignored for too long.* An emotion produced from the churn of the flesh is delivered to a machine, and that machine and its connections manage to produce a flow of images which will arouse some related sentiment in those who watch. The living emotion has passed through a burial ground—and has been resurrected. The living emotion survives as a psychological reality; it continues to exist as a set of images in one's memory which are not too different, as the years go by, from the images we keep of a relative who is dead. Think of a favorite uncle who is gone. Does the apparatus of the mind which flashes his picture before us act in another fashion if we ask for a flash of Humphrey Bogart next? Perhaps it does not. Film seems part of the mechanism of memory, or at the least, a most peculiar annex to memory. For in film we remember events as if they had taken place and we were there. But we were not. The psyche has taken into itself a whole country of fantasy and made it psychologically real, made it a part of memory. We are obviously dealing with a phenomenon whose roots are less defined than the power and glory of king and church. Yes, movies are more mysterious than theater; even a clue to the undefinable attraction of the movie star is that he remains a point of light in that measureless dark of memory where other scenes have given up their light. He has obviously become a center of meaning to millions, possessed of more meaning than the actor next to him who may be actually more attractive, more interesting—definition of the phenomenon frays as we try to touch it. But has the heart of the discussion been sounded? Does it suggest that movie stars partake of the mysterious psychic properties of film more than other actors? that something in them lends itself to the need of memory for images of the past one can refer to when the mind has need to comprehend something new before it? We have to be careful. It is perhaps not so simple as that. The movie star may also suggest obsession, that negative condition of memory, that painful place to which we return over and over because a fundamental question is still unresolved: something happened to us years ago which was important, yet we hardly know if an angel kissed us then or a witch, whether we were brave or timid. We return to the ambiguity with pain. The obsession hurts because we cannot resolve it and so are losing confidence in our ability to estimate the present.

Obsession is a wasteful fix. Memory, when it can be free of obsession, is a storehouse to offer up essences of the past capable of digesting most of the problems of the present, memory is even the libido of the ego, sweetening harsh demands of the will when memory is, yes, good. But the movie star seems to serve some double function: the star feeds memory *and* obsession—one need only think back to one's feelings about Marilyn Monroe! The movie star is welcoming but mysterious, unavailable yet intimate, the movie star is the embodiment of a love which could leave us abject, yet we believe we are the only soul the movie star can love. Quintessence of the elusive nature of film, the movie star is like a guide to bring us through the adventures of a half-conscious dream. It is even possible the movie star gives focus to themes of the imagination so large, romantic, and daring that they might not encounter reality: how can an adolescent have any real idea whether he will ever have sex with a beautiful woman or fight for his life? Nonetheless, events so grand might need years of psychic preparation. It was therefore also possible that the dream life of the film existed not only to provide escape but to prepare the psyche for apocalyptic moments which would likely never come.

Some differences of film from theater may then have been noted. Theater works on our ideas of social life and our understanding of manners. At its most generous, theater creates a communion of bodies and a savory of the emotions—it becomes a feast and a fuck. But film speaks to the lost islands of the mind. Film lives somewhere in that underground river of the psyche which travels from the domain of sex through the deeps of memory and the dream, on out into the possible montages of death—we need only think of any man who was rescued from drowning after he thought he was on the last trip down. Does he ever relate the experience without speaking of the sensation that his life became a film running backward? *It is as if film has an existence within the brain which may be comparable to memory and the dream,* be indeed as real as memory and the dream, be even to some degree as functional. It was as if the levels of that existential river which runs into ultimate psychic states would no longer read as perhaps once it did: sex—memory—dream—death; but now flows through a technological age and so has to be described by way of sex—memory—*film*—dream—death. Theater has to be in the world of manners, but film is in the physiology of the psyche. For that reason, perhaps, film comes nearest to a religion as the movie houses are empty, it speaks across all the lonely traverses of the mind, it is at its most beautiful in precisely those places it is least concrete, least theatrical, most other-worldly, most ghostly, most lingering unto death—then the true experience of the film as some Atlantis of the psyche will manifest itself, and directors like Antonioni and Bergman will show us that the film inhabits a secret place where the past tense of memory and the future intimations of the dream are interchangeable, are partners in the film: there is an unmistakable quality to any film which is not made as filmed theater but rather appears as some existence we call film. That existence runs through Chaplin and *Sunset Boulevard* and *Persona*—it runs through home movies. It was Warhol's talent to perceive that in every home movie there is a sense of Time trying to express itself as a new kind of creation, a palpability which breathes in the *being* of the film. The best of works and some of the worst of film works have this quality. One can even find it for flashes in cranky old battered films of the purest mediocrity late at night on TV, B-films without an instant of talent, yet the years have added magic to what was once moronic—Time is winking her eye as we look at the film. Time suddenly appears to us as a wit.

Of course, there are movies which have delivered huge pleasures to millions and never were film at all, just celluloid theater convertible to cash. Some were good, some very good, some awful, but the majority of motion pictures, particularly the majority of expensive ones, have always labored against the umbilical antipathy of film for theater. They were, no matter how good as filmed theater, never equal to theater at its best—rather, scaled-down repasts for the eye and ear. They had a kind of phlegmatic tempo and all-too-well-lit color which rarely hindered them from reaching lists for the Ten Best Pictures of the year. They were pictures like *Oklahoma!*, *South Pacific*, *The Sound of Music*, *Mary Poppins*, and *The Best Years of Our Lives*. They were even such critical favorites as *Marty*, *Born Yesterday*, *Brief Encounter*, and *The Seven Year Itch*, or *Anne of the Thousand Days*, add *Lust for Life*, *All About Eve*, *Around the World in Eighty Days*, *West Side Story*. All that celluloid was super-technique for audiences who had not necessarily ever seen a play but were constantly nourished in the great cafeteria of the American Aesthetic where the media meals were served up as binder for the shattered nervous system of the masses. To the owners of that cafeteria there was something obscene in the idea that one should not be able to translate a book into a play, film, or TV series—something arrogant, for it would say the difference between the movies just named and films like *Zabriskie Point*, *M.A.S.H.*, *Naked Summer*, *Belle de Jour*,

Limelight, Diabolique, 8½, The Bicycle Thief, The Four Hundred Blows, High Noon, Easy Rider, and *Weekend* were as the difference between crud and sustenance for that ghostly part of the psyche the film was supposed to enrich.

5.

VERY WELL. He had his point at least. There was film and filmed-theater; there were relatively pure movies, and there were moneymaking motion pictures which had almost nothing to do with movies or memory or dream, but were filmed circus for the suckers who proceeded to enjoy them enormously (when they did—for some cost canyons of cash and brought back trickles), suckers who loved them for their binding glue, and the status of seeing them, and the easy massage such pictures gave to emotions real theater might have satisfied more. These motion pictures, made for no motive more in focus than the desire for money, were derived from plays, or were written and directed as filmed plays, they composed three-quarters to nine-tenths of the motion pictures which were made, and they might yet be the terminal death of Hollywood for they were color television on enormous screens and so failed more often than they succeeded; the media were mixed so the messages were mixed—audiences tended to regard them with apathy.

Of course the films he loved were just as often watched in empty theaters, but if he would call upon the difference it was that they were not regarded in apathy but in subtle fear or mixed pleasure or with gloom or dread or the kind of fascination which hinted uncomfortably at future obsession. There was a quality he could almost lay his hands on in movies he admired and so would raise to the superior eminence of Film: they were experiences which were later as pure in recollection as splendid or tragic days in one's life, they were not unlike the memory of some modest love which did not survive but was tender in retrospect for now it lived with the dignity of old love. Such films changed as one remembered them since they had become part of one's psychological life. Like love, they partook a little of some miracle, they had emerged from the abominable limitations of the script, yes, they had emerged out of some mysterious but wholly agreeable lack of focus toward that script in the intent of the director and/or the actor, they were subtly attached to a creative mist, they had the ambiguity of film. For if filmed-theater could sometimes be effective, sometimes be even as perfect and deserving of admiration as *Midnight Cowboy* or *On the Waterfront,* such pictures still had their aesthetic fired by the simpler communication of the theater where relations between actors usually produced a dramatic outcome as capable of definition as the last line of a family fight. "Go to an analyst" turned out to be the message, or "Lover, we'll get along," or "God bless us, we're unhappy, but we'll stick for the kids." If it is theater so rich as *The Little Foxes,* it will say, "I am prepared to kill you, and I will." Since the need of a stage actor is to draw an audience together, his instinct is to simplify the play and concentrate it, give it a single crisp flavor. So theater speaks. Powerfully or with banality, comically, or in the botch of hysteria, it speaks, secretly it almost always speaks vulgarly, for almost always it says, "We're here to tell you something about life. We've got a piece of the meat for you." Of course if it is bad theater, conceived in advance as a television series or any other form of Cafeteria, then it is only there to tell you something about public opinion and how that works at the lowest common denominator. But good or bad, theater functions at its simple best when every resonance of the evening can collect about a single point—that place where the actors seduced the audience to meet the play.

Film, however, is shown to audiences who do not often react together. Some laugh, while others are silent, some are bored. Few share the same time. They have come in on the movie at different places. For film always speaks of death. Theater rouses desires between the living audience and the living actors; film stirs suicide pacts where each individual in the audience goes over the horizon alone with the star; film speaks of the ambiguity of death—is it nothingness we go to, or eternal life? Is it to peace we travel or the migrations of the soul? So the ambiguity of the movie star is essential, and it helps to understand that subtle emptiness which is usually present in the colors of their acting, that pause in the certainty of what they would say, that note of distraction and sorrows on the other side of the hill, that hint they are thinking of a late date they will meet after this guy is gone. Movie stars are caught in the complexity of the plot but they do not belong to it altogether, as stage actors do. It does not matter of whom we speak: whether it is Garbo or Harlow or Marilyn Monroe, Carole Lombard or Myrna Loy, even Dottie Lamour or Gable, the star is still one misty wink of the eye away from total absorption. Even Cagney, phallic as a column of rock had the hint of bells ringing in his head from blows some big brother gave him in years gone by, and Gable's growling voice always seemed to hint at one big hunk of *other* business he would have to take care of in a little while. The charisma of the movie star spoke of associations with tangential thoughts, with dissipations of the story-point into ripples which went out wider and wider, out to the shores of some land only the waves of the movies could wash.

Now, much of that was gone. There were still stars, even in color film there were bonafide stars. There was Catherine Deneuve and Robert Redford and huge box-office familiars predictable as the neighbor next door and twice as vivid —Bob Hope and Lucille Ball for two. If film spoke of death, motion-pictures-for-money spoke of everything which was boring, unkillable, and bouncy, and could be stopped with a switch quick as TV, and was by couples necking in drive-in theaters. The film had also become brands of sex marked R, X, and Hard-Core, the film was epic documentaries like *Woodstock* and *Gimme Shelter,* the film was *Pound* and *Trash* and *Performance,* which some called great and some would not, the film was in transition, the film was in a place no one could name, and he was there with *Maidstone,* caught in the position of talking about a film made near to three years before. Three years was a decade in the recent history of the film. Half of the shock in his sexual scenes was nearly as comfortable by now as the lingerie ads in a fashion magazine, and his emphasis on film without script was evident in small uses everywhere, it had begun for that matter as long ago as Cassavetes' *Shadows,* a film of the fifties he did not particularly remember, but then for that matter, film without script had begun with the two-reeler and the sequence of action worked out on the director's white starched cuff. It was finally not to the point. He had had a conception of film which was more or less his own, and he did not feel the desire to argue about it, or install himself modestly in a scholar's catalogue of predecessors and contemporaries, it seemed to him naturally and without great heat that *Maidstone* was a film made more by the method by which it had been made than any film he knew, and if there were others of which it could be said that they were even more, he would cheer them for the pleasure of seeing what was done. But his film was his own, and he knew it, and he supposed he could write about it well enough to point out from time to time what was special and mysterious in the work, and therefore full of relation to that argument about cinema which has brought us this far, cinema —that river enema of the sins. Wasn't there whole appropriation of meaning in every corner of the mogul business?

II: IN THE PRACTICE

HE HAD, of course, embarked on the making of *Maidstone* with his own money, had in fact sold a piece of his shares of *The Village Voice,* a prosperous and sentimental holding. Not wishing to undergo the neurotic bends of trying to raise funds for a film he would begin shooting in a few weeks without a line of script or the desire to put anything on paper—he looked with horror on such a move!— he had small choice. Who would give him funds on past performance? In his first picture the sound was near to muffled; the second, while ready to be shown in the fall at the New York Film Festival, was nonetheless not yet evidence at a box office, and in fact had been sold to a distributor for fifteen thousand dollars, a small sale even for a movie which had cost no more than sixty.

It was of course possible he could have raised the money. The market was full of profit that year. Risk capital ready for tax loss could have been found. He did not try. There was some marrow of satisfaction in paying for it himself. So he sold a portion of *The Voice* and did not look back. The film was calling to him with every stimulus and every fear. He had, after all, conceived the heart of his movie in the days right after the assassination of Robert Kennedy, a time when it seemed the country was getting ready to blow its separate conventions apart (and indeed he was the man least surprised when the Democratic convention in Chicago had responsible politicians talking of the Reichstag fire). Besides, he was a guilty American, guilty with the others—he felt implicated in the death of Bobby, although he could never name how (short of fornicating with a witch on the afternoon of the deed) he must therefore be so responsible; nonetheless he was, he felt, along with ten million others—perhaps a backlash from years of living with Kennedy jibes and making some of them himself, perhaps from some unconscious delinquency which amounted to more.

In any case, a film he had contemplated for a year, a modest little film to take place in a bar with pimps waiting for their whores and then dealing with them, now turned inside out. He would use that original idea for the core of a larger story, as the sketch of a film to be made by a famous film director within a larger film. This film director would be one of fifty men whom America in her bewilderment and profound demoralization might be contemplating as a possible President, a film director famous for near-pornographic films would be, yes, in range of the Presidency—what a time for the country! Now the last of his elements of plot came into place: there would be an elite group of secret police debating the director's assassination. What an impulse to put this into a script. But writing such a script and managing to direct it would take three years, and call for working with executives in a studio. Others would devour his story and make it something else. He preferred to make it himself, preferred to lose the story himself.

He knew from his experience with *Beyond the Law* (a film of the greatest simplicity next to this!) that when actors were without lines and the end of a scene was undetermined, one did not control the picture. Even if he would be in the middle of the film, would play in it as he had in the two others, would in fact play the leading role of the director (indeed find another actor on earth to even believe in such a role!), that did not mean the film would proceed as he had planned. At best, making movies by his method was like being the hostess at a party with a prearranged theme—at a party, let us say, where everybody was supposed to come dressed in black or white with the understanding that those in black should pretend to be somber in mood and those in white be gay. The guests would of course rebel, first by tricks, then by open stands. A beauty would arrive in red. The party would get away from the hostess constantly—as constantly would she work to restore it to the conception with which she began, yes, she would strive until the point where the party was a success and she could put up with her rules being broken. There would be art in the relinquishing of her strength. If the party turned out to be superb it would be the product not only of her theme, nor of the attack of her guests upon it, but her compensatory efforts to bring the party back to its theme. The history of what happened at her party was bound to prove more interesting than her original plan. Indeed, something parallel to that had occurred with *Beyond the Law*. He had started with an idea of putting together police, a police station, and the interrogation of suspects. But his actors had been as rich in ideas. In trying to keep them within his conception, the picture had taken on a ferocious life.

Yet with *Maidstone* he decided to gamble by a bolder step. Given his plot, he would be obliged to separate his functions as director and actor. It would help his performance if the actor passed through situations he could not dominate because he had also as director had the privilege of laying his eyes on every scene. It was important, for example, that the secret police who would look to assassinate him be able to have their plots filmed without his knowledge. On that account he had assigned directorial powers to several of the actors. They could pick photographers to do their scenes, scenes he would not see until filming was done. So too had he assigned autonomy to Rip Torn who would play Raoul Rey O'Houlihan, his fictional half-brother, an obvious potential assassin in the film—whether Rey would actually strike was tacitly understood to be open to the pressures within the making of the movie. Since Rey would also have the Cashbox, a Praetorian Guard loyal either to Rey or to Kingsley, that must prove still another undetermined element in the film. Of necessity, therefore, would Rey have photographers he could call on. So the company as a whole had five cameras for use—four Arriflex and one Eclair—five teams composed of a cameraman and sound man who were sometimes interchangeable, each team independent, each able to work under available light conditions which might vary from splendid to absurdly difficult, five teams to be spread out on certain days as much as five miles apart, for he had managed to capture the use of four fine houses for the week of shooting the film, an exercise in diplomacy he had not been capable of on any other weekend in his life, he had the estates, and kept them by a further exercise of diplomacy through the weeks before the picture and into the shooting. There were crises every day and he was on the edge of losing more than one set of grounds on more than one day, but the torrent of preparations was on, his energy was carried with the rush—in a few weeks they began with a cast of fifty or sixty (new actors coming and leaving all the time), a capital of seventy thousand dollars, an availability of forty or fifty hours of sound and film, an average of eight to ten hours for each cameraman in a week of shooting which would begin on a light day of work for Wednesday, would pass through the heaviest of schedules on Thursday, Friday, Saturday, Sunday, and finish with light work on Monday and Tuesday, an impossible speed for anyone fixed to the script of a movie as ambitious as this, but he had cards to play. They were his cameramen.

2.

THEY HAD ALMOST all taken part in the making of *Monterey Pop,* which had some of the best cinematography he had ever seen. They had many other credits. That was hardly the point. It was more to the issue that the stodgy unhappy catatonia of the old documentary, where people bearing real names sat in chairs and explained in self-conscious voices what they were up to, had been liberated by the invention of a *wireless* synchronizer between camera and tape recorder. A cameraman free of the caution that he must always move in ways the sound man could follow (since they had once been connected by a leash to one another) was now able to get around as he wished; he could stand on a ladder or slide on his belly, he could walk while filming and turn (years of technique had gone into acquiring a flat-footed walk which might approximate the old camera move on a dolly) but since he was not on tracks or connected to anyone else, so the path could be free in its curve. The eye of the lens could inquire into the scene. The cameraman could even shoot up from the floor between the bodies of men in a dispute or listen to a social conversation from a worm's-eye view beneath a glass coffee table—what play of light on the ashtrays and the highballs! Such shots went back of course to *Citizen Kane*—the issue was that documentary could now be open to subjects which were formerly closed. Since a camera on a man's shoulder was not as intimidating as the old huge camera on a tripod, the subject felt less like a prisoner booked into the stocks of documentary record-taking. Indeed a man who actually reacted to his voice and movements was photographing him. Animation could begin to appear in the face and voice of the subject. So the subjects become more interesting. The documentary moved from the photographing of executives, engineers, and inventors to the faces of slum children playing in the street, or to the study of married couples on an evening at home (and in bed). A world of subjects too fragile in mood for the entrance of heavy equipment, high-power lights, and crews of technicians became available, and people who had formerly been as interesting in front of the camera as slabs of stone began to show a gleam in their façade. But *cinema vérité* still had technical limits which awaited the development of high-speed film with very little grain and better portable sound equipment.

Cinema vérité suffered even further from the basic flaw that people were playing themselves in real situations, and were therefore the opposite of actors. Instead of offering a well-put-together lie which had all the feel of dramatic truth, they gave off a species of fact which came out flat and wooden and like a lie. It was as if there was a law that a person could not be himself in front of a camera unless he pretended to be someone other than himself. By that logic, *cinema vérité* would work if it photographed a performer in the midst of his performance, since a musician in the reverberating cave of his work was hardly himself, he had moved out of daily dimensions, he was a creature in a kingdom of sound. So films like *Monterey Pop* were able to explore the existence of a performer on stage as no fixed camera had been able to do. The crew was small enough to be lost in the lights and the audience. Their lens could move in, retreat, turn away and react, even swing to the beat. Film came back of Janis Joplin and Otis Redding, of Jimi Hendrix and Ravi Shankar which went beyond any film seen before of musicians giving a performance. It was precisely because the cameramen had worked free of the stipulations of a director. They knew more of what a camera could do than any director who had not spent years as a cameraman himself, they had lived in their conscious mind and in all the aesthetic ponderings of the unconscious with the problems of composition in a fast-changing scene, their eye for the potentialities of camera expression was their own.

So far as a man could take a thirty- or forty-pound camera on his shoulder and still see with the freedom of an unimpeded eye they were ready, they could interpret: critical to the matter—they could *react*. It meant musicians could play without a thought of being photographed, and so were never inhibited by the restrictions directors and cameramen working on massive tripods were obliged to impose on a performer's movement.

It had been his own idea, however, that *cinema vérité* might also be used to photograph feature-length movies which told imaginary stories. He had come to the thought by way of his first film. Even if that had ended as a disaster (because the just-tolerable sound he heard on magnetic tape was not tolerable with an optical track), there had been a period in editing when he saw something he had never seen in other film. The actors (he was one of them) were more real, seemed more—it had to be said —more vivid than in other films. He supposed it was because people in fictional situations had never been photographed with such sensitivity before. The camera moved with the delicacy and uncertainty, the wariness before possible shock, that the human eye would feel in a strange situation. The camera had the animal awareness of a fifteen-year-old entering a room rather than a Mafia overlord promenading down a corridor. It made him realize that the movement of camera in conventional film (in filmed theater) had none of the real movement of the eye, just the horizontal movement of vehicles, the vertical movement of elevators, and the turning movement of a door on a hinge. The eye of such cameras moved in relation to the human eye as a steam shovel moves in relation to the human body. The professional camera, however, was smooth, as indubitably smooth as the closing of a coffin lid. If it passed through space with the rigidity of a steam shovel, it did not clank. That, unhappily, was left for the *cinema vérité* camera. The price of greater sensitivity to the unpremeditated action of actors was a set of vibrations, shudders, clunks, plus a host of missed anticipations when the camera zoomed in on the expectation of an interesting response, and the actor, whom the photographer had picked, was dull. Yet even that was cinematically curious once one recovered from the shock that not every instant on screen was shaped into significance. For now the cinematic point became the fact that the photographer could never know precisely what was coming—he was *obliged* to anticipate and he could be wrong: a story began to be told of the uncertain investigation of the eye onto each scene before us. It expanded one's notion of cinematic possibilities, and it intensified one's awareness of the moment. When significant movement was captured, it was now doubly significant because one could not take it for granted. Watching film became an act of interpretation and restoration for what was missed—much as one might look to fill the empty unpainted spaces in old canvases of Larry Rivers—it was also kin to that sense of excitement which is felt at a party when insights are arriving more quickly than one's ability to put them away neatly.

By whatever point of view, he had then a corps of cameramen, and they were equipped to photograph scenes which might veer off in any one of a dozen directions— they were ready to be surprised. It stimulated that coordination between hand, eye, and camera balance which was the dynamic of their art, surprises gave style to the rhythm and angle by which they would move in or zoom away. Once, after an impromptu free-for-all had developed in the filming of *Beyond the Law* with actors' bodies finally locked on the floor like a heap of twist-roll dough shaped for the oven, the cameraman had said, "You know I'd like to cover the camera with a case of foam rubber." And added wistfully, "Then I could just get in the middle of the fight next time." Such ideas carried to their conclusion might slip non-stop miniaturized cameras with built-in lights up the cervix to a baby's fist so the trip through the canal could be photographed, but that was years away from its unhappy debate—for the present he had cameramen who were nimble enough to work in close to a scene and get away (most of the time) without bumping the action or photographing the sound man. Or each other, if two cameras were working different angles.

Later, comparing two men's work on the same scene, he would come to observe that each man had a mode as characteristic as a literary style. The work of one was invariably well-composed, austere, tasteful; another would be alert to the play of forces between two actors—he would have talent for capturing that body language which would most accentuate what the actors unconsciously were doing. Another had little interest in the turn of a scene, but was fascinated with visual minutiae—occasionally his minutiae were more interesting than the scene. Some were best at photographing men, others at studying women or the mood of a landscape. Some were work-horses, some were delicate. Some were delicate and still worked like horses. He came to applaud his cameramen during the week of shooting the film, for there were days when they worked for sixteen hours, bodies quivering from fatigue, yet rallying to steadiness when they worked—the love affair was to go through a turn or two when he sat in a screening room for two weeks and studied the forty-five hours they had brought back, saw the unexpected mistakes, the loss of focus on sudden shifts of action, the edge of the microphone in the frame when the unforeseen move of an actor had flushed the sound man. And wistful disappointments that scenes on which he had counted mightily had lost their emphasis because the cameraman had not seen what he, the director, had seen, had not been in the same state of psychic awareness. And there were miles of footage, filmed in his absence, where the actors had gone wandering and the cameramen had let them, idiocies piled on idiocies, wooden muddy characterless footage, the depression of the cameraman visible in his lack of desire to give visual shape to a tiresome duet. Loss was everywhere in the forty-five hours.

But there were bonuses and benefits where he had never looked. Scenes he had thought uninspired as he played them were given life by the art of the photographer, and scenes he knew were good were made even better by choices of angle he would not have had the foresight to pick himself. If he lost what he desired in one scene, he found himself compensated in another. As the months of editing went on, he would feel at times like a sculptor discovering his statue. The chisel could not go where it wished, but there was a statue to be disclosed if one would follow the veins of the stone. So *Maidstone* began to emerge, not the idea for a picture with which he had begun, but another which had come out of it, a metamorphosis for which he was prepared, since in parallel to the flaws and bonuses of his *cinema vérité* photography the *Maidstone* emerging was as much better than the conception with which he had started, as it was inferior. If it was a movie of another sort than he had first conceived, it seemed to him finally that there were not too many movies like it, for *Maidstone* was a film which had been made out of the materials of its making, a movie which had had almost no existence in plans or on drawing boards or detailed budgets before it was begun, a movie delivered out of film material which had come to life in the heat chamber of seven days of intense improvised and scriptless film-making, so a movie which had a curious first existence in itself not easy to describe and then a later existence which did not come from the stone but the shape of the film-maker's hand. If he had arrived at six or seven hours of footage he considered suitable or agreeable or useful or tasty or splendid or fine or essential, if the smelting had reduced forty-five hours of film to a seventh of itself, there was still, he knew, a length to which the material must shrink by way of brooding, rubbing, and polishing, by elucidation then de-infatuation with pieces of film or conceits of story he had loved too much at first to relinquish. It would be a work of months, and then finally of a year (and a second year to follow) of mistakes and losses, blunders and mislaid gems of film strip, but when done, it would be his conception, he would by then have *written* a movie using strips of film rather than words, a movie different from the film anyone else would have made out of the same six or seven hours of usable film, would have written it as uniquely, and differently as any one writer would have been from another writer if both were working on the same topic and had the same dictionary. It was his film. He had framed some of the language, and others had framed the rest of it for him, but by the time he began his editing, it was all part of the same dictionary; he had created *Maidstone* out of the given; so it was entirely different from films which had devoted their effort to creating the given from a script, then nailing it up according to plan.

In the act of this most particular film-writing, his pencil become the size of an editing machine,* he discovered where he thought the nature of the film might lie, and so tried to end with a film which would be in itself the nature of film, a metaphysical dumpling of a remark which is close to indigestible. Does it make it easier to suggest that even as an angel may be the nature of goodness and beauty, so to look at an angel is to obtain a picture of humans from heaven? By analogy he wanted a film which would live in the mind like a movie star, that is he wanted the film itself to be the movie star, some evocative, ambiguous presence which was always suggesting the ghostly but most real intrusion of the *special* existence of cinema.

3.

BUT HE anticipates. He has come to the peroration before he has reached the middle. It is a natural mistake for a film-maker. A novelist learns early in his career that beginning, middle, and end are a part of literary time, and cause direct notice when shifted, but in film no time exists but the order of progression. A film is made by one piece of film being stuck onto the next and that is the only scheme of time which prevails. Afloat on the full tide of a film we see an actor who looks twenty years old. In the next cut he looks sixty—we do not jump immediately to the conclusion that it is forty years later, no, we may have to recognize it is his idea of himself forty years later, or his recollection of a previous life when he was

---

* With the advent of electronic editing from video tapes the notion of *writing* one's movie out of the film at one's disposal— since it promises to be quicker and easier—becomes next to inevitable.

sixty. Indeed it may be a shot of his grandfather—we wait for the next cut. If it explains nothing, merely goes off to further adventures of the twenty-year-old, the isolated cut has its peculiar existence—it is a warning or a symbol or an omen, something!—it sticks with its incomprehensible flash even as we have flashes in life of people we know well who are seen for an instant doing something we cannot comprehend—the town patriot sticks his tongue out at the flag: next moment he is, as always, smiling on his cigar. Did we see the tongue go out or did one crazy cell in our own head imagine it? That is a fair preparation for film. One can put anything next to anything in film—there is a correlative in some psychic state of memory, in the dream, the *déjà vu*, or the death mask, in some blink of the eye or jump of the nerve. So one can work whole stretches of film free of any thought of the story. A piece of film can be put next to another piece of film regardless of plot —it will work or it will not work. Of course, this is exactly the place where the mystique of film begins and one starts to talk of its nature. Every beginner of a film-cutter becomes willy-nilly an amateur philosopher about the time he recognizes that you cannot attach one piece of film to another simply because it makes sense for your story. If the cut is poor, the screen will jump. A virtuoso can make it jump to one side, then to the other—that, too, is a psychic state the film can offer, but it is like the dying spasms of a broken tooth—can the average film afford such pain?

No, there was a syntax to film movement. The slow sweep of a man walking to the left and out of the frame could be followed by the sweep of another man walking to the right. If the tempos were similar, the movement was restful. If the second man walked faster than the first the logical expectation was for a faster and more intense scene on the third cut. Some action would obviously be getting ready. What it was would hardly matter. A fight could follow between two men or two dogs, an airplane could dive, a train go by, or a woman could scream, then turn immobile and the freezing of her movement would go into the strictures of the scream. You could do anything in film if you could do it. Of course, some cuts were vastly better than others but led you to more exquisite troubles since several beautiful cuts in a row awakened expectations which oncoming material would have to satisfy. If there was nothing that good to follow, it was like stopping in the middle of the act.

On the other hand, mediocre cuts could follow one another, each cut more or less endurable, until suddenly a cut would go dead. The cut had seemed reasonable for the plot but it left a feeling in the lungs analogous to breathing the exhaust of a bus. Cuts were like words. You could put many an ordinary word next to another word but you could not put them all. If your last name was Klotz, you might call your son Chris, but you would not call your girl Emerald, not unless your ear and the ear of fashion were in a special little race that year. Godard made jump cuts in *Breathless* which no one had been able to endure before, did it out of all his experience as a cutter, and from his artistic insight that the verboten had moved to the edge of the virtuoso. Yet, you may be certain the twenty precise cuts before the jump cut fed subtly into it, if indeed the jump cut had not become the particular metaphysics of that film.

Still, some cuts work, some do not. Some cuts work in extraordinary fashion. One cannot understand why two pieces of film otherwise unrelated seem agreeable next to one another, even appear on screen with that same unfolding of mood the sun suggests as it works at last through a cloud. Poetry is working. A few words which had little to do with one another are now enriching each other. Peerless grapefruit peel! In color film the effect is twice to be noticed. For the syntax of good movement can be reduced by the color, or, since color film is easily as malleable to editing as black and white, an otherwise indifferent movement will be given resonance by the shift of color. It does not matter what is used. A good cutter with enough film can cut a run of images which will give pleasure to an audience. If there is no story present, no other exposition or logic than the aesthetic of color, composition, and movement, then there is a length to such a film, and it is not usually more than a quarter of an hour. Give a hint of story, however, and the interest of the audience might ride for twice as long. The good cutter is like a very good skier. He does not study the trail ahead, he sets out down the mountain, makes his turns as they come, does his checks, his drops into the fall-line, his traverses into the hill, then tips around and down again. It is beauty to watch. If we add the knowledge that he is in a *race*, the beauty is hardly diminished and our tension is certainly increased. It is not unlike what happens when a hint of story is added to film montage.

Now, however, create a complexity for which film is uniquely suited. Offer a situation where the film seems to tell the audience the skier is in a race, then a minute later seems to indicate he is not in a race. All the while we are following his descent—now the race seems to be on again. To the attention and irritation of not knowing which situation is real, and to the beauty of the photography, have been added ambiguities of context. A fine slippery shiver of meaning comes over us because the situation has altered a little faster than our comprehension of it. Film can offer such sensations as no other art.

If, then, he was ready to start with a conventional, even supercharged movie plot (which he knew would be quickly warped, intensified, dissipated, and altered) and if he was equally ready to throw a Colosseum fodder of actors almost totally untrained into such maximum circus, it was because he had learned that improvised scenes with *cinema vérité* photographers gave many more opportunities to the cutter than the choices open to a film editor who was working on a movie whose rushes came off a script. For, whether trained or untrained, actors in any improvised scene had hardly any more idea of what the final relation of their scene would be to the eventual movie than a man in a love affair may know if his woman will be with him for the rest of his life. So there was an indispensably intense air of the provisional and the real to the actors' work. They were not present to send off signals, as actors with a script must unconsciously do, that the end of the scene was near. Therefore, any improvised scenes which worked in whole or in part, which is to say had vitality or flashes of vitality, always gave some interesting ensemble of movement that could be used as the springboard for a quick or curious cut to the tempo of other actors in other improvised scenes which were also working well. Indeed, one could cut away from a continuing scene at any point—for the script was still to be put together. That was a choice which film with a script would rarely offer. With script, each scene was staged and thereby necessarily acted with its little unconscious beginning, little middle, and little end. Options for interesting cuts were on the consequence blocked. A scene which ended with a book being laid with measured finality on a table tended all too often to require an ensuing movement equally full of the slow and the stately. That was legitimate if the flow of the movie called up such a tone, but it was deadening if the next scene in the script wished to get off to a quick start. That next cut could no more ignore the last pause than a conversation could glide over the remark that a friend had passed away.

Improvisation obviously gave more freedom to the cutter, so much in fact that the logic by which one began to connect pieces of film to each other seemed at times to arise out of the very logic of film—even if the logic of film was a concept as deeply buried as the logic of language and so might have to wait for its first tentative elucidation by a semantics of film. What appeared as the immediate difference was that with improvisation and free cutting the story was not obliged to be present as the walls and foundation of a movie, but rather became a house afloat on some curious stream, a melody perhaps on which many an improvisation was winging—it was as if story now had the same rare relation to film images bear to language. The influence of story now was partial, not whole. For even as language consists of both the concrete and the abstract, of particular images and also of concepts which have no image, so any logic of film could contain elements of natural story and elements of movement which were opposed to story or simply indifferent to story. The *resonance* of film, the *experience* of film—words were of diminishing use here—seemed to derive from some necessary tension between the two, even as language seems to require that we pass from image to concept and back.

But if *Maidstone* (as a prime example of the logic of film) is already once removed from words, it is twice dangerous to keep speaking of it without offering a little more of the particular experience which produced it. If the obvious suggestion arises that the experience resides in the nature of improvisation, one may be forgiven the excessive symmetry of next suggesting that the concealed properties of film and improvisation are parallel (which is why they may belong together). We look at film, any film, and chaos is to a degree ordered. (We can, for example, photograph a wastebasket and it has become more an object of order than it was before.) We know we are looking at a life which is not quite life although it will certainly shift the way we live. So improvisation also orders chaos—gives its focus to random emotions—also becomes a life which is not quite life, and yet, even more than film, improvisation suggests it is indeed ready to become life. Ready to become life? Are we speaking of the moment when a fantasy, which is to say a psychological reality in the mind, transcends itself and becomes a fact? We are probably back to the last afternoon in the filming of *Maidstone*.

4.

GIVEN HIS THEORIES on improvisation, there was a problem to filming *Maidstone,* and it was fundamental. While he took it for granted that any man or woman who could talk under stress was usually ready to burst forth with an improvised characterization (almost as if the ability to act, like the ability to make love, had been waiting for its opportunity), still one could never forget that art is art and self-expression is all too often therapy. The need therefore was to have a scheme which would keep the improvisation from flowing over into a purge. Some con-

straint had to be found for each scene; ideally, an over-
lying constraint had to be found for the entire film. In
Beyond the Law, the problem seemed to solve itself. Being
a policeman or a suspect arrested for the night was apparently one of the formal, even primeval scenes of the
unconscious. None of his actors had trouble believing
they were either policemen or under arrest, indeed his
actors were richer in the conception of their role than the
author would have been if he had written it for them.
Nor had his presence as a director even been necessary in
every scene. He had filmed most of *Beyond the Law* on an
unrented floor in a seedy office building. It was perfect for
giving the sensation that one was upstairs at a police
station. Since he had set up interrogations between his
detectives and suspects in separate rooms, three camera
teams worked apart from one another in the different
interrogation chambers. As in a police station, detectives
came in and out, questioned a man, took off. Other detectives came in. After a period of filming, the floor of the
office building might as well have become a police station.
There was a babble of sound throughout, prisoners were
arguing, weeping, protesting, going silent, detectives were
bellowing or intoning charges, sounds of a beating in one
room were agitating an unstable prisoner in another. Half
the movie had been filmed in two nights, filmed on a sea
of sound and cinematic sensations.

Now, however, he was ready to make a film of no
simple premise and much complexity. Ideally, many of his
scenes would be subtle. Any demonstration of the value of
making a movie by this method would depend consequently
on how elusive, light, and sinister, were the effects
obtained. The proof that his method had resources could
only be demonstrated by capturing delicate qualities which
none but the most carefully prepared films had hitherto
provided. Since he also wished his picture to be nothing
less than comic, farcical, sexy, on the edge of horror, and
with more than a hint of the ghostly, the concoction
would not be automatic to obtain.

Still, he believed he could get it if he could only provide
an atmosphere, some pervasive atmosphere, in which his

untried actors would arrive at a working mood. For *Beyond the Law,* his police station had provided that atmosphere, provided it as forcefully as a movie being made in a coal mine. But *Maidstone* would be filmed half in open air; the other half would take place in living rooms and sitting rooms which were models of the exotic or the established. Any prevailing atmosphere could not be simply created by an ideal set—rather it would have to come from the presence of the film-making itself descended as some sort of spirit-resident upon Easthampton, a somewhat frightening film to be certain for its central figure was a man living in danger of assassination. Since improvisation was never dependable, far from it! the theme was uneasy to all. Murder is another of the primeval scenes of the unconscious. The impulse, however, is guarded by bulldogs in fifty restraining collars—murder was not likely to occur this week on the cheap. Nonetheless, it was only a month and a little more since Bobby Kennedy was dead. That was a thought which lay heavy. Another was the instability of fifty or sixty actors, some white, some black, all congregating and soon fornicating in two small hotels. Nor were the scenes to be played likely to reduce any tension.

He was not so paranoid as to see the venture daring more than a most risk-diminished form of Russian Roulette. Surely, not more than one chance in a hundred, say at the most unlucky, one chance in ten of a real assassination attempt, but whatever the percentage, the practical working movie point was that one percent of real risk introduced a paranoid atmosphere of risk which might be put at twenty percent. And that was a percentage to work with, a percentage to keep the cast in a state of diabolical inclinations, some sensuousness, and much dread. How could legitimate fear not arise that some innocent bystander, some bit actor, would catch a maladroit effort at assassination intended for another? So a presence for the film had been created. The fear of assassination hung over the cinematic shooting like the faintest luminous evanescent arch of the ineluctable beyond, yes, some pale shade was there, some representative of the ghost-world of film there along with everything else, along with chaos, cries of love in the grass, and the physical grind of the work, the rush of scenes, the military madness of schedule. Actor and quartermaster, general, production engineer, and the only substitute for a script girl, he had himself more roles than ever before in his life, and staggered through *Maidstone* with the brain of an exhausted infantryman, his mind obliged to work as it had never before, work constantly and without respect for its age, vices, and sedentary habits. Since he also had not slept more than four hours a night for the last two weeks of preparation, keyed to a pitch which if struck could have given off a note, he was speaking slowly for the first time in his life, his brain too used-up to talk fast—the picture was later to prosper as a result since people for once could hear him! —he had nonetheless to wonder at the oddest moments (for there was an unmistakable rainbow of fear and elation in the breath of his chest and it did not leave until the film was done), had to wonder why he was taking such a peculiar chance, which if small was still unnecessary, and knew it had some murky soil of congested roots in the irrational equation that Bobby Kennedy had taken a large chance for a large goal, and he must—in some equilibration of all the underground pressure systems of guilt—now find a way to take a smaller chance for his own private goal, suspected he would never have made this movie or even conceived of it if he had not sat in a room with Bobby Kennedy a month before his death and failed to realize danger: that the man was in mortal danger. So he had a motive not far from obsession: one could return to it over many a year.

Of course his other motive was professional, even elegant in its professionalism. For the fact that he not only made a movie about a possible assassination but gave it structure as a game, even offered the fierce privilege of autonomy to actors who were scheming up plots for his possible cinematic assassination, must also mean that the presence was now being fortified. So he played his part, acting for at least half of his working day rather than directing, his own role certainly helped by that delicate baleful edge of presence which might lead to artwork, a debacle, or outright disaster. He had no idea what was being hatched about him. He knew only that a variety of large and little plots gave every indication of generating some focus, some steam, some point of a gun, and went through days with staggering schedules, his best reason for speed the instability of the situation. His actors were in for a long weekend. Any longer and the presence would explode or worse, appear absurd, dissipate. Each day in fact he was losing actors, some from frustration, some from fear, some of them good, some promising. Potentialities of story which hung on their presence would have to take a turn. He was not worried at that, not worried by any item of plot or arrival or departure. They would, as he told the company, take B if they could not take A.

So he lived on the fine fever of making the film, hardly aware of any hullaballoo but his own; he was become a powerless instrument of his own will, pleased at bottom to be out of touch with two whole sides of his film—the assassination activities of the secret police, and the possibly murderous ones of the Praetorian Guard—stayed like some animal in a zone of hunters knowing the great fatigue of a high alert, his senses an adrenalin of warnings whenever Raoul Rey O'Houlihan-Rip Torn was near, for he knew as if Torn were his true brother that the web of intriguings had Torn at the center, that if psychic biddings and curses were flying like bats through the ranks of the company, then Torn was the hole in the roof where they all came in. What pressure! What logic and what torture! What impulse! For Torn was more than an actor, he had in addition to debate his attempt to be the assassin. The vanity of a proud actor, not nearly recognized sufficiently for his talent, for the remarkable force of unholy smolderings he could always present, now had to become a vanity pushing him to take the center, to move from that secondary position of acolyte to the leading part, and preempt the part, be the killer who invaded the hill. Yet he was also first centurion of the guard to protect Kingsley from the point of the threat, and took his mission seriously, yes, with all the seriousness of a profound actor steeped in his improvisation. Ready to die in order to save Kingsley, he was also ready to kill him—anything but to have the quiet insistent pressure of the picture pass into nowhere, all threats stilled, his own role stilled.

So the night before the afternoon on the grass, the night of the assassination ball became O'Houlihan's high agony. Raoul Rey-Rip Torn had become the center of the film, the focus of every loyalty to the director, yet the wild card in every plot, since it had become an unspoken convention that the attempt of assassination would be on the night of the ball (as if actors in a sustained improvisation ganged naturally to the idea of a focus of plot), so in the hours of the night as the party went by, plots arose and were shattered or missed, or evaded, the director never feeling more real in the role. Uncertain of the size of the attempt, or whether the attempt was even yet to come, not knowing if he played in a game which was a real drama, or worked for a drama just so absurd as a game, he did not accept the more obvious gambits of plot which were offered him. If obvious, they seemed ridiculous, as though one gave assent to pressing a button which would release a boxing glove in one's face. No, he took up posts, or promenaded for two hours—impromptu bodyguard always about him—hung in the situation for two hours, and the time done and the party over, spoke now not to Rey but to Rip as if the movie were finished, as indeed he thought it was, for nothing but a few elements of the dream called "The Death of the Director" would be filmed on Gardiner's Island with the company next day, a day in fact for picnic and celebration that the film was over. His own danger had been as one part in one hundred or less, but he was glad it was done, and so said to his fictional brother, "I don't know if we got anything tonight, but it's still all right," thinking to himself of the dozen different ways he could cut the film (his security residing in a documentary on the making of an unsuccessful film since there was always footage of his own voluminous directions to the cast) and so saying, went to bed and finally to sleep, and the next day found to his horror that on Gardiner's Island

after the lecture of orientation was over that the presence
of the dread was returned, but now shorn of elation, shorn
of a rainbow. There was something heavy, then awful in
the air, he knew he was in more physical danger than at
any time before, and as Torn came walking toward him
across the green, hammer dangling from his hand, he
remembered taking off his black leather vest and holding
it like a short folded cape in lieu of a better weapon, and
after the fight, too furious to speak to Torn for many a
month, outraged that Torn had broken the unspoken convention of their film—that violence cease with the end of
the filming of the ball—was yet obliged to discover in the
months of studying his forty-five hours of reels that his own
blunder had been enormous in giving so much autonomy
to Torn and the other assistant directors. The work they
had done was by sections good, but not finally good enough.
The buried half of the film he had been waiting to see
would remain for the most part buried. He had been left
with the most embarrassing work of all, an ego trip, for
he had been the hardest-working actor in the film, and so
the film was his, it was all too unhappily his, and all too
much of him, since that was the part which unfortunately
worked the best. Torn had therefore been right to make
his attack. The hole in the film had called for that. Without
it, there was not enough. And with it—he glimpsed as he
worked each day with his editors that a film was emerging
which he would yet be pleased to call his own for it was
a mysterious film and became more mysterious as he
thought on it. It was reminiscent first of the image he had
held of the ski race which was on, then declared off, then
put on again—the film shifted from context to context in
modes as obsessive and haunting and *attached* to memory
as those recollections of indefinable moments between
sleep and a dream where context shifts, only to shift back
again—we are in the dream . . . no, it is the edge of
day. So Proust had floated his reader on a hundred-
page procession of state from sleep to wakefulness into
sleep.

In *Maidstone* the context moved into some other place.
It was a film about the surface of reality and the less visible

surface of psychological reality. For if everyday reality was a surface, or a crust, or a skin, psychological reality was a balloon which lived as a surface so long as the air of belief was within it. And since he had come to write his *Maidstone* after all the film was in, he chose the mysterious shifting character of its surface as the subject, and looked to show just how many of its realities were psychological realities which could suddenly be exploded and then where had they gone? What was left of such reality? It was a project he could never have commenced with words, nor even with the fiction of a story, but *Maidstone* had been filmed not only as an imaginary event but as a real event, and so was both a fiction and a documentary at once and then become impossible to locate so precisely, for what came nearest to the hard hide of the real? Was it Norman Mailer, the self-satisfied director, instructing his cast for the last time, or was it the suddenly real head of Norman T. Kingsley that Torn as suddenly attacked. (Yet his hammer had been held carefully on the flat to reduce the damage.) For if the attack was real, the actor upon whom it was wreaked should not be, and would not be unless the attack became fiercer still, fierce enough to kill him indeed. Then Kingsley would have become undeniably more real than Mailer.

It was a species of realization—that the hide of the real remains real only so long as the psychologically real fails to cut into its existence by an act which makes psychology real—the tongue would twist in its turnings on such a philosophical attempt faster than the film. For it was possible *Maidstone* inhabited that place where the film was supposed to live—that half-way station between the psychological and the real which helped to explain the real. As time went on, he saw that the cutting he did by newly acquired instinct was with purpose, and had a logic to reveal the topography of that half-way station. For *Maidstone* kept promising developments of plot which never quite took place, even as we travel through our lives forever anticipating the formation of plots around us which do not quite form. We are always looking for real stories to ensue which never exactly enact themselves as we expect, yet we still work at such times as actors in the real story of our life, pursuing roles which can become our life at any instant the psychological can become the real —as occasionally it will. For out of fifty stories in which we are at any instant enmeshed (fifty sets of expectations that next week we fall in love or tonight we go out and get drunk and have a terrible fight), not three times out of fifty, not two, nor one does the expected event occur. And then it does, it happens, it takes place out of the stored force of all the denouements which did not take place. So Torn attacked out of all the plots of other actors, Torn became the presence of the film, the psychological reality that became a literal reality out of the pressure of all the ones which did not. So that film about a director who would run for President became instead a photographed event of simulated plots and threats kept under high pressure by the curious curse of playing with photography of the female in the act of love, of playing with the curse of love which is gone, of playing with the curses of matrimony, yes, that film of an event which was a thousand events (of which nine hundred and ninety had small issue, or none, or were never photographed) became at last a film of the ineffable shimmer of reality, even became, as its director had wished, the star itself. Then it was that the presence of the film crystallized into the *geist* of *Maidstone*, Rip Torn. A superb actor was at a pitch of intensity and so revealed the premise on which a film had been built, even offered the essence of a method which could yet become the future of the film. For is it not a common premise to many a lover of movies that the hidden wealth in every strong-box of the cinematographic are those sequences of footage where the event has been innocent of script and yet resonant with life? Of course! We are talking of nothing other than movie stars in frames where the mood has been pure. Mood is our only acquaintance with the sensuous properties of time. And film is the only art which can search, cut by cut, into the mystery of moods which follow and accommodate one another; film is the only art which can study sudden shifts of mood which sever the ongoing river of time a fine film has set in flow. So we search for the pure in film as we search for the first real tear of love. We are a Faustian age determined to meet the Lord or the Devil before we are done, and the ineluctable ore of the authentic is our only key to the lock.

(Continued from page 6)

and dream, sex and death. According to Mailer, the partic-
ular agent of the film's power to speak to "the lost islands
of the mind" and the main object of the obsessive interest it
fosters is the movie star, whose "presence"—so intimate and
yet remote, so distinct and yet reverberative—suggests the
very essence of film itself. Mailer's intention, then, was to
create such a presence, to arrange matters so that it would
happen, not by means of any one star but by the improvisa-
tions of cameramen filming persons who were acting out
their obsessions with sex and death; in short, "to end with
a film which would be in itself the nature of film."

Mailer's commentary on Maidstone *is also a commentary*
on the making of art. One point in particular stands out in
this reader's mind. In the course of financing, organizing,
shaping the situation of the film, directing, acting, and then
editing, he is always moving in the direction of what can-
not be foreseen, of what must be risked. Partly this is due
to his theory of film, which gives the largest possible scope
to chance, improvisation, instinct. But it is also due to a
desire to make the precipice of failure real and near, to
work on its edge. So "A Course in Film-Making" is also a
course in the dynamics of risk, which is, one gathers,
what Maidstone *is also partly about. That Mailer is inter-*
ested in this theme is hardly news; but we are once again
indebted to him for portraying how close to the nerve
(in both senses) interesting art must work.

While we did not plan to publish Mailer's essay with
Stanley Cavell's "Some Reflections on the Ontology of
Film," that's the way it has happened, and we think that
readers will profit from it. Cavell approaches the nature
of film from a different direction, defining it by way of
photography and against painting, in order to establish the
particular properties of the medium. Yet there are a re-
markable number of points at which his account and
Mailer's of the phenomena of film touch and illuminate
each other. What is most striking about Cavell's essay is
his concrete and coherent description of the particular
visual reality of film and its relationship to the "real world."
What happens to reality when it is projected and screened?
What does the silver screen screen? Bogart, a building:

what subtle and mysterious relationships these bear to actors, buildings. "Screen," "frame," "projection," "presence": the very words hint at the puzzle that Cavell locates at the heart of the film experience itself.

TS

OUT OF THE THOUSANDS *of poems, or texts in the shape of poems, submitted every month to NAR, how—by what impossible filter, what empirical or abstract grid pressed upon the helpless, aspiring words—are the eighteen or twenty poems selected that appear in each number? By—precisely—submission: by yielding to the impulse itself as it appears, written (or, so often, merely typed up, blocked out in every sense) on the page. To have patience with the poem! Patience is, literally, suffering, and the poem—each poem—is to be suffered gladly for the sake of that moment when it will, or when it may, speak.*

For that is how the winnowing is done, the triage *made: a moment comes in the course of reading a poem (and of course there must be enough of a poem there to permit the moment to come: reading 500 haiku is to be nibbled to death by fish) when the language of the poem ceases to be the language of the author of the poem, when indeed the language of the poem becomes only—only!—its own, an autonomous voice heard in the passion, or the refusal of passion, which its energies inaugurate and sustain.*

It is for this moment that every poem submitted is scrutinized; it is for the transition—yes, the going-over of utterance, the passage out: so that what is acknowledged is no longer a woman who hates her marriage, a man disgusted with his city, but a poem which is content (true aristocrat) to be known by its actions, not to be recognized by its intentions. What is looked for, listened for, is the moment—it is a consummation: a marriage certainly, but also a using-up, an extinguishment—when the poem is no longer the self-expression of its author, but rather something

*restored, to its author and to every reader, on the other
side of language: which is to say, of course, on the other
side of death.*

*Noticeable, even evident, I think, in the poems that
appear in* NAR, *and almost programmatically in the poems
that appear in this number, is another kind of transition or
accommodation: between the private self and the public
imagery, between what is given out (by the culture; by
what we have come to call the media, though in a society
such as ours they have ceased to be means and have become ends) and what is taken in (by the separate, even
by the isolated or imprisoned, person). The movies, television, the newspapers—how many of the poems here come
to terms (and the terms arrived at* are *the poems)—with
these promulgated emblems of ourselves; how many of the
poems are encounters, when they are not conflicts, between
recognition and ignorance, between an unacceptable public
image and an unsuspected private identity—image prod-
ding identity to account for itself by its very rejection of
that image.*

*It will be seen that what is advanced as the strategy of
choosing these works—the transformation of what is merely
identifiable as a person into what is an identity as a poem
—as well as what is advanced as a characterization of the
works chosen—the encounter between self and surround,
between world and will, in which what was merely uniform
becomes unified—are indeed something of the same thing,
and anything but "advanced." Rather, the effort, the sub-
missive hope, on the part of the poetry editor—and partiality
is the first acknowledgment, paraded, clung to, saved—is to
make his method coincide with Goethe's declaration (was
it advanced two hundred years ago?) that the beginning
and the end of all poetry is the reproduction of the world
outside by means of the world inside.*

                                                        RH

CONTRIBUTORS

A. Alvarez has published several books on poetry, most recently *Beyond All This Fiddle*. "Sylvia Plath: A Memoir" will appear in his book *The Savage God: A Study of Suicide* to be published this winter by Random House.

Donald Barthelme writes that "Alexandria and Henrietta" is "part of a novel, more or less." His story "Robert Kennedy Saved from Drowning" appeared in *NAR 3*. *City Life*, his most recent collection of stories, was published by Farrar, Straus & Giroux.

Richard Brautigan is the author of *Trout Fishing in America, A Confederate General from Big Sur*, and *In Watermelon Sugar*, among other books. *The Abortion: An Historical Romance 1966* was issued last spring by Simon and Schuster.

Rosellen Brown's stories and poems have appeared in *The Atlantic, The Nation*, and *TriQuarterly*. *Some Deaths in the Delta & Other Poems* (University of Massachusetts Press) was a National Council on the Arts Selection 1970–1971.

Lennart Bruce has contributed over a hundred poems to various magazines. Collections of his work include *Making the Rounds, Observations*, and *The Mullioned Window* (Kayak Press).

Emile Capouya is literary editor of *The Nation*. He has written for *Commonweal* and *Saturday Review*. A previous essay on anarchism, "The Red Flag and the Black," appeared in *NAR 6*.

Turner Cassity, author of "The Airship Boys in Africa," the longest poem ever published in *Poetry*, and founder of the Atlanta Zeppelin Club, is a librarian at Emory University in Atlanta. *Watchboy, What of the Night?*, a volume of his poems, was published by Wesleyan in 1966.

Stanley Cavell teaches philosophy at Harvard and is the author of *Must We Mean What We Say?* (Scribner's). The essay in this issue has been adapted from his book *The World Viewed: Remarks on the Ontology of Film*, which Viking will publish this fall.

Robert Coover's fiction includes *The Origin of the Brunists*, *The Universal Baseball Association*, and most recently *Pricksongs and Descants*. He is at work on plays and "a new book-length fiction."

Rick DeMarinis has contributed poems to several magazines, including *Poetry Northwest* and *Massachusetts Review*. He teaches at San Diego State.

John DeWitt teaches at Drexel University in Philadelphia. He has previously published in *The Lace Review*.

Roy Edwards lives and paints in New York, where he has shown with the West Side Artists and at the Rose Fried Gallery.

Irving Feldman has published several collections of poems, most recently *Magic Papers* (Harper & Row, 1970). He is at work on another volume, to be called *Marvels, Elegies, Insults*.

Andrew Fetler, recently writer-in-residence at Amherst, teaches at the University of Massachusetts. His fiction has appeared in *The Atlantic* and other magazines; his novel *The Travelers* was put out by Houghton Mifflin in 1965.

Peter Handke is the young Austrian playwright, poet, and

novelist. *Kaspar and Other Plays* (Farrar, Straus & Giroux, 1970) will be staged by Peter Brook in the near future.

John Hollander's most recent book was *Types of Shape* (1969). Atheneum will issue *The Night Mirror* in September.

Shirley Kaufman contributes poems to many periodicals; *The Floor Keeps Turning*, a collection of her work, was published by the University of Pittsburgh Press.

Norman Mailer's movie *Maidstone* will be shown in New York in October. The essay in this issue will appear with the screenplay, *Maidstone: A Mystery* which New American Library will publish in October.

James Martin has been a lobsterman, surgical orderly, student at Colby College, and contributor to *Poetry*, *New England Review*, and other magazines. He now attends Boston Divinity School.

Heather McHugh recently graduated from Radcliffe. She has published poems in *Poetry Northwest* and *The New Yorker*, and poems and articles in *Mademoiselle*.

William McLaughlin teaches high school in a Cleveland suburb. Over the last few years he has written on education as well as contributed poems to various magazines.

Ursule Molinaro is the author of *Green Lights are Blue*, *Sounds of a Drunken Summer*, and *The Zodiac Lovers*. She is currently working on a book about numerology, *Love by the Numbers*.

Herbert Morris's poems have appeared in *Southern Review*, *Hudson Review*, *Poetry*, and other periodicals.

D. F. Petteys has contributed poems to *Confrontation*, *Salmagundi*, and other periodicals. He teaches contemporary literature at C. W. Post College of Long Island University.

Ralph Pomeroy has published poems and art criticism in *Art Forum, The New Yorker, New American Review,* and other magazines. Abrams will issue his book on Theodoros Stamos in the spring of 1972.

Nicholas Rinaldi's poems have appeared in *New England Review* and other magazines. He teaches creative writing at Fairfield University in Connecticut.

Michael Rossman lives in and organizes out of Berkeley. "Introduction to Dome-Building" will appear in somewhat different form in his book *On Learning and Social Change,* to be published by Doubleday later this year.

Ira Sadoff teaches at Hobart and William Smith colleges, Geneva, New York, where he is co-founder and co-editor of *The Seneca Review.*

Constance Urdang is the author of a collection of poems, *Charades and Celebrations* (October House), and a novel, *Natural History* (Harper & Row).

Complete Your Set of NAR

Issues 1–10 are going out of print. We have a limited supply available at $.75 each.

☐ NAR #1 William H. Gass *In the Heart of the Heart of the Country*, Philip Roth *The Jewish Blues*, William Mathes *Swan Feast*, Stanley Kauffmann *Drama on The Times*, Benjamin DeMott *"But He's a Homo-Sexual . . . ,"* Grace Paley *Faith: In a Tree* . . .

☐ NAR #2 Alan Friedman *Willy-Nilly*, John Barth *Autobiography*, Nat Hentoff *Reflections on Black Power*, Arlene Heyman *Strains of Iris*, Günter Grass *Four Poems* . . .

☐ NAR #3 George Dennison *The First Street School*, Donald Barthelme *Robert Kennedy Saved from Drowning*, Paul West *A Passion to Learn*, Philip Roth *Civilization and Its Discontents*, Albert Goldman *The Emergence of Rock* . . .

☐ NAR #4 Robert Coover *The Cat in the Hat for President*, C. C. O'Brien *Politics as Drama as Politics*, Mordecai Richler *A Sense of the Ridiculous*, Alan Lelchuk *Of Our Time*, Richard Gilman, *The True and Only Crisis of the Theatre* . . .

☐ NAR #5 Pat Watters *"Keep on A-Walkin', Children,"* Wilfrid Sheed *Eugene McCarthy*, Eric Bentley *The Unliberated University*, Jay Neugeboren *Reflections at Thirty*, Jules Siegel *The Man Who Believed in Christmas Trees* . . .

☐ NAR #6 Jane Jacobs *Why Cities Stagnate*, Ellen Willis *Lessons of Chicago*, Robert Stone *Porque No Tiene* . . . , William H. Gass *We Have Not Lived the Right Life*, Eric Salzman *The Revolution in Music* . . .

☐ NAR #7   Kate Millett *Sexual Politics*, Rosalyn Drexler *Like . . .* , Michael Herr *Illumination Rounds*, L. Woiwode *Don't You Wish You Were Dead . . .*

☐ NAR #8   John H. Schaar *Reflections on Authority*, George Dennison *On Being a Son*, Eric Bentley *Theater and Therapy*, Theodore Solotaroff *Silence, Exile, and Cunning*, Ernest Callenbach *The Death of the Movie Aesthetic . . .*

☐ NAR #9   Alfred Chester *The Foot*, Theodore Roszak *The Artificial Environment*, Samuel R. Delany *The Unicorn Tapestry*, Richard Gilman *Jerzy Grotowski*, *Symposium: The Writer's Situation I . . .*

☐ NAR #10   Philip Roth *On the Air*, William H. Gass *In Terms of the Toenail: Fiction and the Figures of Life*, Arno Karlen *The Guardian*, Jules Siegel *Family Secrets*, *Symposium: The Writer's Situation II . . .*

New American Review
Subscription Dept., Simon & Schuster, Inc.
1 West 39th Street, New York, N.Y. 10018

Please send me the copies of *New American Review*
 checked above.

Enclosed is my check for $_____, calculated at $.75
 per copy.

Name _____

Address _____

City _____ State _____ Zip Code _____

Please allow at least three weeks for delivery.
Offer good in United States only.
Foreign orders: add $.50 per copy for postage.